The
Frog Who
Dared to
Croak

The Frog Who Dared to Croak

Richard Sennett

Farrar, Straus & Giroux

New York

Library of Congress Cataloging in Publication Data
Sennett, Richard
The frog who dared to croak.
I. Title.
PS3569.E62F7 1982   813'.54   82-1508
                                     AACR2

To three friends

William Shawcross
Victoria Glendinning
David Rieff

The
Frog Who
Dared to
Croak

On March 5, 1973, a messenger appeared at my office and left a large parcel. It had no sender's address, nor did it have any postage. Undoing the wrapping, I found within another parcel, on which was written, "Mr. Fentimen, this comes to you from Tibor Grau. Just before he died, he asked me to send it to you; he said you would want to publish it." There was no signature. This inner package contained various scraps of paper, old envelopes, the dust jackets of books, each covered with writing in a fine hand. It also contained police reports, newspaper clippings, and some official documents. All these proved to be by or about Tibor Grau.

A publisher is often bombarded with unwanted manuscripts. I would have thrown the package away, had I not noticed that name. My predecessor at the firm had published three books by Grau, each on philosophical subjects. I once heard Grau lecture, and knew a little about his life: that he was a philosopher who had been embroiled in revolutionary politics in his native Hungary at the end of the First World War, that he went to Moscow in the late twenties, and that he survived the purges of Stalin by dint of personal cunning and intellectual compromise. The reviews here in England during the forties

The Frog Who Dared to Croak

and fifties, when we published him, spoke of Grau as a brilliant man ruined by Communism.

The materials I received are Grau's own story, as he wished it to be told. There is little about philosophy in them; they are of a more personal, shocking nature. They reveal a soul struggling with fear and despair. Grau provided only one key to the manner in which he wished this jumble of scraps, letters, and documents to be published; he numbered them, roughly in chronological order. All Grau's "private" writing, on the backs of envelopes and the like, is in German. I am responsible for translating these materials. Letters and official documents in Hungarian have been translated by Professor Paul Szentibos. Edtorial comment has been kept to a minimum; I have, however, taken the liberty of dividing the documents into five parts, and a certain poetic license—justified, I hope— in the book's title.

> *Herbert Fentimen*
> *Parkes and Fentimen Ltd.*
> *London*

July 1976

Part One

First Steps

1

As I often tell the young ones, you must lie to survive. But what is a lie? The deceiver must know truth, in order to mask it. Ontologically . . . but I mustn't get lost in all that. I simply say, you must lie to survive, yet there comes a time when you want to be candid, just like wanting to practice your French after not speaking it for years, just to say what you think and what you are. If only you can.

For instance, a friend has brought back from the West a book partly about me. *Three Revolutionary Philosophers of the 1920's: Malek, Grau, Krys* the title. Below us the author, Richard Pribel. Above us, "Voices beyond the West" editor, Gordon Reed. But editor, subjects, and author are all crowded up at the top of the cover, which is some sort of abstract-decadent painting. In fact, on the back of the book, below the part that tells a lot of lies about me, it says: "The cover of this book is one of a set of ten, comprising the covers of the first ten titles of the 'Voices beyond the West series.' The set combines to form the whole painting, and can be arranged in an unlimited number of different patterns."

So Mitsuki, Borz, Dimitrov, al-Ginna, Faduk, Malek, and myself (Krys was an absolute cretin; including him was disgraceful), we can be moved around like so many chess pieces to make a different pattern in the child's game which is this abstract-decadent painting, this "Voices beyond the West" cover. But probably the others never had to learn to lie *well*, so I can't be shuffled with the rest: the piece that sticks out—or is it that "sincere" writers don't have to worry about the jailer reading over their shoulder?

How remarkable! Professor Pribel writes that after I fled to Moscow in 1929 I began writing stuff that was "complete rubbish. While initially the most talented of the three, Grau in the Soviet Union became a Party hack." Pribel, I was cold. People were dying of cold in Hungary, in the East, many people. The price of coal in Russia was "Belinsky and Herzen were the precursors of the method, the culminating points of which are marked by the names of Lenin and Stalin." Not a great price, surely. And then I was canny.

I was canny. I wrote in my book on Kant: "Capitalist dialectic constitutes a constant play upon the heroics of self-deception such that being and appearance become synonyms," which is, all right, rubbish, but then on the very next page I wrote: "But the bourgeoisie is constantly engaged in a struggle to remove from being all those aspects of appearance which suggest that being itself is a pseudo-problem." Anybody with half a brain can see the second cancels the first, you just need the eye of a tyrant's subject. My eyesight is superb, it always has been. In fact, my uncle Bela used to say that the Grau boys would go to their graves without glasses, although in my right eye I have a kind of tick which is distracting when I do highway driving, but the point about Pribel is: a face without a mask gets frostbite from the cold.

2

It is rather difficult, I find, to say what you are on the backs of envelopes, but I must write this on what can be easily burned. Yellow pads of lined paper do not burn quickly enough, when you hear them knocking at the door and you have to move fast. I mean, you get the pad burned through, but the little tips don't burn smoothly away and so when they come into your living room they see and they know you've been burning *something*, and to arouse suspicion is nine-tenths of the way to being caught. So I am having to write on the back of old electric bills, on envelopes which contained notices of the next Academy of Literature meeting, and so on.

That was a close call. I'll just dust this sugar and flour off these scraps, and then they will be just as good as new. My housekeeper is intelligent; in fact, she may be termed indispensable.

What happened was this: I went out, and they went in. The flat is four rooms in a row, with doors from one to the next and no outside corridor. The scraps were in a Sèvres jar my father gave me, in room 2.

The moment she opened the door to them in room 1, which is a kind of antechamber, she knew what they were, even though they wore workmen's uniforms and said they'd come about a gas leak somewhere in the building. I have arrived at a high enough position that in dealing with me they have to pretend a little. And of course my housekeeper had to go along and pretend that they were what they pretended; otherwise, they might have become quite angry. So she said, "You can work in this room to start, but mind the pots and pictures"—I keep only ferns and photographs of relatives—"because today is dusting day and Professor Grau hates things out of place, or smudges or fingerprints on anything."

They agreed to be careful.

Then she went into room 2 and took out that white linen rag she is always carrying about the flat and that smells so (and she is right, I can't stand clutter or even disorderly smells, so I don't see why she doesn't get a new rag each week), she took out the rag and poured an immense amount of furniture polish on it and began doing the piano, all the wooden chairs, and the Sèvres pot in which the scraps were. When they came into room 2 the smell was overpowering, of course (she could have been considerate and used less); but this gave her the excuse to hold the Sèvres vase and buff it furiously, as though she were a cleaning maniac, while they worked their way through the rest of the room. Then she looked inside the vase and cried, "Yech, ashes—always dirt after Bulgarian visitors" (we had had in, the day before, two Bulgarians, writing on "Mime and Man"—not bad), and she took the offending object off to the kitchen. Now she knows they will examine the trash; indeed, they usually tell the janitor not to use the incinerator beginning two hours before they plan to come. So she took the vase to the kitchen and stashed my scraps in the big jars of flour and sugar, smoothed over the surface, then dug into the garbage pail, which, thank God, had not yet been emptied, routing around in the potato peelings and coffee grounds until she found the ends of the cigarettes which the Bulgarians in fact did stink up the house with, put the cigarettes at the top of the garbage pail, and washed her hands. In fact, she was washing her hands just as one of them came into the kitchen to ask her something, so she by chance put the finishing touch to her performance of a fanatic maid.

These dear envelopes, bills, and wrappers of course are new and something of a risk, but I am hardly the sort of fellow to be ordinarily unprepared for such visits. I always make sure there is *something*, a little something about which a person could logically feel guilty, and which might even be used to pressure him, but which is safe politically and betrays no dangerous thoughts. When they find this little indiscretion, then they have an object to bring back to their chiefs, the whole operation has been a "success," and they usually hurry through the rest, because there is nothing more boring than leafing through the pages of book after book, and a man, even one of them, is anxious to get home to his dinner. I usually leave a pornographic novel (heterosexual and sadistic, the safest genre) in room 3. Such novels are easy to buy.

I am just forty-five years old.

3

While Grau opens his story in the 1950's, the previous document must have been composed around September 1, 1938, since our records show that Tibor Grau was born

The Frog Who Dared to Croak

on September 1, 1893, forty-five years before. The documents Grau has labeled "3" have precise dates later in 1938. They are printed laundry forms that Grau has filled in.

MARSHAL BOBRINSKOI HAND LAUNDRY

Man's Inventory
December 29, 1938

Item	Number	Price in Kopeks
Shirts	2	boyhood traumas
Pants	2	months in jail
Suits	1	marriage
Vests	1	affair
Hats (dry-clean fur)	no	children
Hats (dry-clean cloth)	1	revolution
Other	3	good books

MARSHAL BOBRINSKOI HAND LAUNDRY

Man's Inventory
December 31, 1938

Item	Number	Price in Kopeks
Shirts	endless	boyhood traumas
Pants	2	months in jail
Suits	1	marriage
Vests	not enough	affairs
Hats (dry-clean fur)	no	children
Hats (dry-clean cloth)	any	revolutions?
Other	1	good book

First Steps

The first list of his life Grau drew up represents, evidently, a more "official" version than the second list. The second version is the story told in these pages.

4

This memoir of childhood was written in a school examination book. The book (consisting of ten ruled pages stapled together) was folded in four so that it formed a tight little packet about three inches square.

My own father was born a Court Jew. That is, he was a Jew of such eminence that people overlooked the fact he was Jewish. He directed the Budapest branch of the Vienna Kreditanstalt. The biggest bank in the Empire. In fact, he was such a special Jew that the Emperor made him a noble, and so I am really von Grau, and I used to sign myself that way in my articles, before I understood what it meant to be a "von" who had become a "von" in living memory. But my father was never ashamed of this title—neither ashamed nor proud. He was ironic about it, and that made it possible for him to play the part of the nobleman gracefully. He enjoyed it when other people's servants announced him as Margrave von Grau, but at the bank he never used the title, because it suggested, he thought, a lack of seriousness.

He was a short man, with the family's very good eyesight, not terribly handsome, because he had a hairy mole on one cheek. He had, I remember, very strong thighs, almost like straight-sided tubes. We walked every day together, and because of these legs of his I was usually panting along. Although, really, he was ironic about everything when he talked, not just himself, he was very serious about walking. Good for the circulation; toughens you.

We lived in a rather small house (considering our position). It was in Buda, and it had a large, walled garden. My father was not only ironic, he was restrained; he disliked showiness. I had a little "writing room," as studies used to be called, at the top of the house, and when I published my first essay (I was seventeen), he was ironic about that, too. Well, I had something worth showing him.

I was seventeen in 1910. In 1912 I wrote *The Dead Angel*, and the next year I wrote a two-volume work about poetry and society, two volumes coming to one thousand pages. All this is true.

My father liked to be with me. He enjoyed watching me play, which was unusual in those days, because fathers were supposed to be too grand to waste time with their children. He never actually picked up my toys. Later he enjoyed talking to me about my studies, although I think he enjoyed this less than watching my play. He could become passionate about writers who interested him, like Goethe, Schiller, and von Kleist; he could also be elaborately deferential to me when we talked of writers whom I liked and he did not—modern writers. Then he was on guard: irony. But about the toys.

When I was six, I was given a large stuffed brown bear named Henry. Like all large stuffed brown bears, Henry had buttons for eyes, and these buttons gradually came loose on their threads. My father took quite seriously my fear that Henry was going blind and explained that Henry had magic eyes, with holes in the middle made

First Steps

expressly for needle and thread, and that, if I didn't cry
and kept my hand steady, I could restore Henry's sight
and my brown bear would be forever grateful.

When my father came home at the end of the day,
he would watch from a window while I took Henry for a
walk in the garden so that Henry could do his business
there. The gardener was told to rake up a little mound
of leaves and clippings behind some azalea bushes and
keep it trim; I would place Henry on top of the mound,
and when it seemed to me he had had sufficient time to
go to the bathroom, I would take him off the mound and
we would walk back into the house. The family would
then have high tea. Among families like ours, tea was an
elaborate affair, with three-tiered tea-cake stands holding
an immense number of small pastries, cookies, and can-
dies. But, for the children, the display was sheer agony;
we were supposed to choose just a few things, not eat
everything in sight; it was a lesson in discipline. If you
got beyond yourself and grabbed an extra, the others
looked at you silently, steadily until you put it back. Sometimes I wished that someone, Nanny, Father, my aunt
who came to live with us when my mother died, would
have shouted at me "No!" or slapped me, but in families
like ours, this was not done . . .

I woke up last night from a nightmare in which
Znadov was lying on a tea-cake stand like the one I wrote
about yesterday. I often have this dream, and I must be
careful with my memories or I shall dream about Znadov
every night. I attended Znadov's trial earlier last year.
They read out the charges, asked him then to stand up
in the dock, and then there was silence in the court;
Znadov was supposed to confess to the charges and the
trial would be over. What seemed like hours passed by,

while Znadov stolidly refused to play the game, and then the judge cleared the courtroom of spectators. My teacake stand dream is terribly obvious, isn't it? The trouble is, the charges against Znadov were true . . .

Aunt Doreen was born while her parents were traveling in Ireland, which is why she had this foreign name that is so hard to pronounce. She was therefore known from her childhood on as Agnes, but the children had to call her Aunt Doreen from the time we began our English studies. She was convinced that the correct pronunciation of her name, once achieved, would be the key to perfecting the whole of one's spoken English, and so she would repeat it endlessly to us, and we would respond by making it increasingly strange and un-English, until we were sent out of the room.

Aunt Doreen had absolutely conventional views on almost all subjects, and she looked upon her own peculiarities, if she remarked upon them at all, as correct, acceptable conduct. Thus, if she gargled a little water at the table just before retiring with the other ladies at the end of the meal, she never failed to urge the other guests to do the same, as the only possible means of effectively warding off contamination of the mouth by food poisons during a meal. Not, perhaps, reassuring advice to guests, but she carried it off. In one way, however, her views were radically and self-admittedly "advanced," views which had a profound effect upon my life.

Most children of my class were educated by tutors until the age of eleven. These tutors were usually ignorant and stupid, hoping to pass the time with their charges with a minimum of noise, teasing, or, indeed, talk. Aunt Doreen recognized how stultifying they were and insisted that my sisters and myself be sent to the local school. She maintained, and my father finally agreed, that the inter-mixing of classes would be less harmful to us than the anesthetization of our young minds via some Miss Borgward or Mr. Painter-Haynes. And so, at the age of seven . . .

You think you have to come to the end of it in yourself, and then you find always a little something more. It may be no more than a mild longing that, suddenly perceived, enlarges itself into an aching desire for what does not exist *now*, it may be no more than the memory of some little injury, some little cruelty that you performed in the far past, a cruelty that is now enormous because you cannot recover it, since your mother is dead. Dead. These tricks of the demon are all gathered in his power to infect memory. I can resist anything I have to face in the present; I am strong. But when it is over and becomes a thing of the past, then the demon strips away my armor and my very own memory, in so soft a voice, shows me in the act of resistance what I lost, ignored, or hurt.

At the age of seven, I entered St. Stephan's School. It was two kilometers from the house, and I was driven there in the closed coach the first three years I was at the school. On my tenth birthday I was given permission to walk to school. St. Stephan's School, despite my father's fears, was not really a school for workingmen's sons; few of the proletariat's children could afford school over work, even though primary schooling was obligatory at that time in the Dual Monarchy. And of course, the authorities really had no desire to educate the poor—too much danger that the more educated the workers, the more they would be prone to revolt. But there were still three or four poor children in our class of forty, and more important, there were perhaps fifteen children from a stratum of life that both my father and my aunt detested—the petite bourgeoisie. I never heard my father make fun of an uneducated servant or workman about the house, but I heard him mock quite often, in that quiet way of his, the pretensions of the local dentist or of the middle-aged clerks and accountants at the bank. He would say, when the dentist came to the house (as they did in those days), that the "gentleman," using the English word, had come about my teeth. The children of the despised class were now among my peers, and I remember that even then, even when we were seven years old, they who had to walk to school would watch the arrival of my coach each morning with a kind of angry envy. The dentist-clerk-boys. They were on the threshold, they envied. When I was finally allowed to walk to school, it was a great occasion for me, for now I could be just like everyone else.

But I wasn't like everyone else. I was a little genius. When I was eight or nine, and had had two years of teachers making a fuss over me, I thought I was smarter because I was richer. I was certainly smarter than all the dentist-clerks, but it wasn't my fault. I remember saying to myself over and over again, "It isn't my fault: I can't help it, really I can't—here, I stole some candy from home, have it." Although sometimes this worked, other times nothing would. And of course, it was the acceptance of dentist-clerks I wanted; kids as rich as I was didn't matter, because they took me just to be one of them who was a little odd. If I had been weak or scrawny, perhaps it wouldn't have mattered, because then they would have had something over me. But I was also stronger. At eight,

First Steps

I could do fifteen chin-ups. Richer. Smarter. Stronger. They were loathsome, the dentist-clerks; later they had pimples, but they resisted me. I had to have them, to conquer them.

Finally, I did have one of them, in the basement of the school, where we had gone to fetch some charcoal for our sketching class. He let me feel his penis; there was no hair around it, the skin was smooth, soft, and moist. I knelt down and he let me tuck his penis into my armpit, which was also smooth and moist, and I could feel the blood vessel throb in his penis as he grew hard. But then we were caught. The drawing master had come downstairs to find out what was holding us up. This incident was never mentioned by anyone to anyone ever again.

The wheel of memory. At the time I felt no shame. Then the wheel turned; I was older, and the silence surrounding our discovery filled me with anger. Then the wheel turned again, a revolutionary turn; I came to Russia. I learned defiance means death. I remember this encounter now only with regret, with longing. What if the wheel of memory has stopped? This is what the demon wants: every memory filed clearly, like the rows of books at school arranged neatly along one wall, in order of increasing difficulty. The wheel stops, and the prisoner has no escape. Every day of his existence controlled, then filed away precisely when it is over. So that the prisoner, you see, can remain free inside only if he can spin the wheel of memory, keeping alive the secrets that keep him sane. And this is why the leader-guards hope to break down the prisoner's last defenses by saying, "You are lying! It wasn't really like that."

5

Despite Grau's hint in the second laundry list that he intended to tell the following story, he did not do so until he was an old man. Perhaps a feeling of relative security may have prompted him to fill in the picture of his youth. When Grau wrote this document in 1960, he was living quietly in retirement near Budapest. In any event, unlike the first four pieces, there are no creases or folds on these pages which indicate the author sought to make them a hidable packet.

I have just received in the mail the following letter; it comes from the *International Dictionary of Socialist Biography*. I am not asked to provide my biography. Those deemed worthy of such an honor will of course have it created by committee. No, I stand on a somewhat lower rung of eminence and I am addressed as follows:

Dear Comrade,

As part of our effort to document the international history of socialism, we are soliciting from a number of figures who played a constructive role in the early years of this century responses to the following questions: What steps first led you to Marxism-Leninism? What were your first activities in the movement? How do these activities appear to you in retrospect? As our leader, Comrade N. S. Khrushchev, indicated at the Party Conference in 1956, the period of the cult of personality arrested attention from the many and varied efforts to build

First Steps

socialism in this century around the world; attention was unfortunately focused on the activities of one man. Part of the rebirth of our movement consists of a renewed knowledge of the past. We know you are in a position to give untold unborn generations valuable information about your own activities, and invite you to do so. A reply is expected (double-spaced, typewritten) by March 1, 1960. If your recollections are included, you will receive a leather-bound copy, free of cost, upon the date of publication. Please send your document to: Hungarian Subsection, International Dictionary of Socialist Biography, Ministry of Culture, Moscow, U.S.S.R. Thank you,

The Committee
January 1, 1960

P.S. This letter is also an authorization to your local Committee on Ideological Standards for one-time, ten-copy use of the mimeograph machines. You may keep two copies.

There are many things which I savor in this letter. From the literary point of view, the phrase "arrested attention" is good; there were so many attentions arrested. "Untold unborn generations" is also good. Notice that the committee does not promise to print everything it receives. The notable with a past will learn that his life is acceptable if he receives a leather-bound book. ("But, Postman, I'm sure you must have a book package for me; everyone else has already received theirs.") That is the way of our committees. Increase anxiety and you create the desire to be approved. Finally, consider well the postscript. This is a valuable letter because it gives the bearer the right to use the mimeograph machines. These days,

The Frog Who Dared to Croak

all worthwhile literature appears in copy rather than printed form; the trick is to get access to the locked quarters in which the copying machines are kept. Once inside, you can always find someone to bribe—two shoe coupons, or even one, for ten minutes when the guardian turns his back—and so reproduce your real work for others to read. This postscript, properly understood, is a stirring call for freedom of expression, and it is this stirring call to which I respond. I will draft a private answer to the committee's first question, "What steps first led you to Marxism-Leninism?"

My "first steps" toward Marxism-Leninism were taken in the Budapest Municipal Park. I was prowling the park every night when I was fifteen and sixteen—that is, prowling every night my father and Aunt Doreen were dining out. On those evenings, I could excuse myself by saying I was going to the library. I was so brilliant that I could do all my schoolwork in one or two hours in the late afternoon; this left me free evenings.

You must understand what it means to be thin and muscular at the age of fifteen; what it is to have a father who viewed one's own premature entry into the adult world with regret; what it is to feel at that vulnerable age radically unlike other boys. The cocktail mixed out of these elements is the desire for a passionate embrace with someone who is large, mature, and wears a rough cloth. The desire flickers like a beacon between two islands. I will be more precise. I wanted in the park to let large, mature, rough men know I was available. I wanted them then to approach me, never to take the initiative. And, to be even more precise, I wanted them to hug and embrace me. I was revolted by the scenes of fellatio and worse that I witnessed in the dark hours in

First Steps

the park. I wanted simply to feel an alien body warm against mine. The dangers of exposing myself to pursuit, and then exposing my genitals—through quickly unbuttoning the trousers of the other person and having him unbutton mine, then pressing our two secret, moist parts together—these dangers aroused me. Then as now the police were on the lookout for such encounters; they would ignore a burglary, a fire, in order to hide for hours in the dark so they might spy out two men hugging each other. And I will remark in passing that they seldom arrested the criminals before the act was consummated; they watched as long as possible.

But the real dangers in the park did not come from the police. We knew their habitual routes, and could easily outwit them. For instance, the police were unwilling to patrol the hollows in the park, for fear of getting mud or muck on their boots; we naturally sought out these depressions for our prowling. The real barrier to sex was the crowd of poor people who slept in the parks because they could not even spare a penny for a space on the floor in one of the slum barracks.

Before the First World War, about half the land in Hungary was owned by six families. Most peasants were landless; they worked at most four months a year, and that during the harvest season, when they drove themselves like animals twenty hours a day. The result of this situation, which had existed since the fourteenth century, was mass stupor. In the last century, perhaps a generation before I was born, a glimmer of hope came to the peasants. The city of Budapest began to grow. People in the countryside heard of a second cousin who had found work twelve months a year sweeping the streets, or they heard what was the true fairy tale, of someone who had come from nothing to own enough to open a shop. And so this mass, like an immense wave of lemmings, swept toward Budapest, with no real prospects save the faint hope in the mind, the glimmer, that generation after generation of misery might magically end. Nothing, at any rate, could be worse than remaining as they were. Or so they thought.

It is hard to assay the varieties of human unhappiness. I have always imagined that hope extinguished is worse than unchanging, blank despair. At least I imagine this to be true from the way I heard the dispossessed talk in the Budapest park.

I would hear the men curse through the trees. Let me explain that I mean this hearing in two senses. I was prowling around in the hollows, looking for figures, like statues, who in the darkness did not move. When a likely one came into view, I too would become a statue, waiting, hoping, and afraid. The voices of the men who had found no work that day would drift down into the hollows. These voices came through the trees in another way as well. The stories of people tying themselves to trees in the Municipal Park to sleep are true. Here is what they did: a man would take a long length of rope and pass it back and forth across several branches, forming a web on which he would place a blanket. This was his bed. You could walk under the trees and hear snoring, moans, and even lovemaking above, if the branches were strong enough to support two people. A few policemen, for sport, would sometimes climb up the tree trunks and cut the ropes.

Each year, Budapest would fill up with more and more people looking for work. The wages for servants steadily declined as the supply increased; a man could do industrial labor, if he were lucky, for fifteen hours and

First Steps

be paid the wages that would buy him a sticky bun. Soon the municipal bathhouses were filled to overflowing, people sleeping in the baths themselves, until a city ordinance decreed that only those who could prove they had lived in the city for five years were allowed to enter. In the country, a starving man could steal easily enough apples or grapes to fill his belly. The famous pear trees of Budapest were guarded by a special detail of police. The crisis of capitalism, as the very poor understood it, was a matter of a place to live. The crowds in the park were the most visible sign of this crisis.

Now, to people like me those men appeared not only as intruders but as opportunities. Revolted or bewildered as a young peasant lad might be by a city boy who wanted to have sex with him, the peasant was soon aware that this boy also had money, and if the peasant did what the city boy wanted, he would be paid far more in fifteen minutes than he could earn in a week of drudgery. And I must point out that many of these peasant boys, especially if they had come to Budapest alone, had no particular moral feelings about the attentions of other men. In fact, given my own desires simply to rub against them, they often found the sexual act comforting—an embrace of comfort and security on their part, an embrace of passion on mine.

Now I am ready to begin to explain my first steps toward becoming interested in Marxism. These steps occurred when I began to feel such love for some older boys that I wanted to stop paying them, imagining that they would freely return my feelings. The more of their sufferings I saw, the less these peasants appeared to me as statues; having admitted them to my world, I wanted true love, sexual contacts freely exchanged out of mutual sympathy. By the time I was sixteen, I knew several of the peasant boys who regularly slept in the park; I considered them friends. With one or two, I found that this new feeling of mine was returned. I suppose they did believe that I, although younger, would still act as their protector in the city; they were, moreover, so helpless. But many of the others refused to embrace me when I said I did not want to pay them. They could not understand what I was talking about. They needed money to eat and to buy liquor. My allowance was their lifeline. This I wanted to cut in the name of love.

Pavel, for instance, I had been supporting with a tenth of my allowance—and my allowance was not large by bourgeois standards of those days. My allowance would buy, say, ten books a month and give me enough for coffee at a café every day with my friends. With a tenth of this amount, after two months, Pavel was able to send the rail fare to his sister and her husband to come to Budapest. Pavel was large; he had a line of hair running straight up from his crotch over his navel to his chest, where the hair spread out in a luxuriant fan. Sometimes after we had finished, he continued to hold me, and to stroke my hair. Often we would talk; he would tell about his village, recount his fruitless attempts to find work on the tramways of Budapest (ill luck that he attributed to a spell cast by an uncle), and ask me endless questions about our house and family life. How many rooms do you have? How many pigs do you keep in your back yard? Why, please, are there different glasses for different colors of wine in your family? How big was the chicken your father "gave" yesterday (the head of the house, in Pavel's mind, always "gives" food at dinner) to your family? How much do you pay

First Steps

the priest to say special masses to bring good fortune? I answered these questions as best I could. When I thought a true answer would make no sense, or be embarrassing, I made things up, as about the number of pigs in our back yard. I told Pavel, simply grasping at a number, we had sixteen, and he looked at me as though I were the scion of an Oriental potentate.

After two months, I was feeling so close to Pavel that I said I wanted to make love freely to him, without paying each time. I carefully explained my reasons for this, my belief that passion soon evolves to a higher stage of friendship, and so forth. I was not totally blind, I knew he needed money. I proposed that from time to time I would make him gifts; I wanted us to make love, however, without feeling that I had to pay for each caress.

Pavel's inherent dignity showed in his response to this speech of mine. He did not become angry, nor did he attempt to wheedle the money out of me. He cast his eyes to the ground, twisted the front of his shirt, and began talking to himself about how he would explain to his sister and brother that there was no more money.

"Look," I said, "we don't even have to make love. We can meet and talk, and occasionally I will make a present to you; I will put it in an envelope and it will be a wonderful surprise."

Pavel said to me that this wouldn't do, he had to have enough pennies each day to support his sister and her husband, who were also living in the park; he had family responsibilities. This I was too young, too wealthy, to make any sense of. I wanted Pavel to say, "I love you, I will do anything for you." I now realize he wanted me to say, "I will make it possible for you to hold up your head to your sister and her husband."

The Frog Who Dared to Croak

Pavel and I parted early one summer evening. The next night I went back to his tree, to tell him I would pay, but he had gone. An old statue of mine told me he had moved to a different part of the Municipal Park because he had found an insurance clerk, aged about forty, and made an arrangement with the man.

My experience with Pavel was repeated with a few others. Some became angry; one threatened to tell my father what I did at night, since this man had followed me home once and found out my name. Another beat me up. The angry ones I reasoned with, until their anger turned to disgust. The one who threatened blackmail I dared to do it; he couldn't write, and he would never get past the servants' door. I fought the one who tried to beat me up; we made so much noise that policemen appeared on the rim of the hollow and we both ran away.

By the end of my sixteenth year, when I was advancing to the upper level of the Gymnasium, I had left off night visits to the park. My desire had waned. I would lie in bed at night stroking myself, thinking of the many men I had had. I would think of them, and the pleasure would come, and I would smear my belly with it, and then I would sleep.

And this is how my interest in Marxism began, gentlemen. I read your literature in sympathy, but I found out very little that bore directly on my experience.

A scene has often repeated itself in the course of my lifetime. A meeting will be called in which both intellectuals and members of the Party from proletarian backgrounds will be assembled. At some point during the meeting, the worker Party members will begin accusing the intellectuals of not really "understanding the masses." This accusation has, the innumerable times I have heard

First Steps

it, so constant a form, so monotonous a set of elements:
you do not understand what it is like to be hungry for
days on end, you do not understand what the muscles
feel like after working twenty hours like an ox, you do
not understand the children crying because they are
cold in a house without coal. It is like a cherished opera
aria which one could play on the gramophone over and
over. When I listen to this aria, which never fails to produce its intended effect on others of guilt and submission,
I think of the following things, which I am sure the proletarian accusers do not think about. I think of how one
gradually comes to savor the odor of dried urine, and how
this odor, compounded daily because my men were not
allowed to bathe, gradually transforms itself into a bouquet. I think about what it was like to kiss a man who
has been drinking bad brandy in order to keep warm,
the smell of bad breath and brandy also transforming
itself into a bouquet. I think about those tired muscles,
although the muscles I knew were not the arm muscles
of men fatigued by labor, but the thigh muscles of men
walking the streets looking for work, and I think of Imre,
for instance, who thanked me once for massaging his
thighs because his wife was too prudish to do so. And
most of all I think about the voices coming through the
trees, the voices complaining, cursing, then later, as
though they also had an aria to sing that followed a regu-
lar form, becoming the sounds of sleep and of dreams,
the song of men on their blankets up in the trees. These
thoughts have insulated me from the sting of proletarian
accusers.

I have said that at the end of my sixteenth year I
ceased to go to the Municipal Park; my pleasure became
solitary. Shortly thereafter, I began to experience a ter-

The Frog Who Dared to Croak

rible itching in my crotch. I went to the school doctor, a very elderly man, who promised never to tell my parents. I did not at first understand this statement. He then explained to me fully the nature of crab lice, asked how I had acquired them, asking about this or that whorehouse in town, was the woman large, small, fat, black-haired, and so on. Evidently, as the school doctor, he had an intimate knowledge of the people boys were likely to meet. I could not confess. I made up a prostitute, drawing the character from *Nana, La Dame aux Camélias*, and a few other books I had read. "Oh yes, I know that one," he said, to my immense relief.

After I was cured, I forced myself to spend evenings with girls. I went through the motions, but my heart was not in it. The curious thing was that my female companions quickly perceived my distance, and this very aloofness excited them . . . Martha, for instance, whom I danced with frequently at parties. I want you to hold me closer, Tibor. If you like. She smiled. My parents will be in the country this Friday, let's go to a café. Good, but I must be home by ten. She looked intent.

I imagine the editors of the *International Dictionary of Socialist Biography* will receive approximately five thousand versions of the following story: the youth reads *The Communist Manifesto*, light thereupon shines into his darkened brain, this work leads him to the political journalism of Marx and Engels, and finally he discovers the magic mountain of *Capital*. Had I any intention of sending in this account, the editors would receive from me something quite different. I missed my men. School dances had no romantic aura for me; the other boys would strut about like turkey cocks, telling lies about their conquests. I missed my men. And yet I could not bring myself to go back to the park, nor would I go to the public toilets at the edge of the gasworks, where the most sex-crazed went. I looked at the turkey cocks parading their thin bodies beneath their ever so neat clothes and I thought, if only you knew how sordid life is, if only you knew how sad and impossible it is to love. If only you knew . . .

It was at this time I began living with my men in crowds. Nothing more. No demands. I wanted to hear at least an edge of passion in their voices, if not the same I had heard before. I hated how the people of my parents' world took the silence of servants, coachmen, and workmen for deference; I knew my men were boiling inside with rage. I went to demonstrations.

Today we think of the political protests before the First World War as a preparation for the changes that have since come. But if the truth be told, these events were often a farce. I've saved the poster from my first one in 1911. It reads:

THE WORKERS AND STUDENTS OF FREE HUNGARY CALL UPON ALL OPPRESSED PEOPLES TO ATTEND A MEETING OF MASS SOLIDARITY IN THE STADIUM PARK ON DECEMBER 6, AT 1800. FREEDOM TO THE PEOPLE!

I remember that I arrived early at the stadium, a huge open park, because I was afraid I wouldn't get a good seat and hear the speakers. I have always been punctual, punctual to a fault. I expected masses of policemen, Hussars on angry, dancing horses, and the people armed with sticks, or stones held under their cloaks, a possibility of blood and fraternity, and I wanted to be there.

So I arrived well in time and what did I find but twenty or thirty people milling around looking lost, a few policemen occasionally directing fierce glances toward them, but then gossiping among themselves about the races. Well, I thought, the factories close at five (very early you see, because they had no electric light, and so people could finish in winter whenever it was dark); I thought: soon the masses will arrive and we will have people packed in here and excited simply because there are so many of us.

But not more than another twenty or thirty people came. There were no chairs, and this surprised me; I imagined it would be something like an evening at the opera. The fifty of us stood in the center of the plaza, and then the organizing committee arrived, five fat men dressed in black with dirty white collars and fine watches. The first of the five fat men stepped up on a box and began to speak in Croatian. It turned out he was a Croat nationalist who had come as a gesture about the very technical problems of organizing the national struggles of the Croatian People's Republic after the revolution. Since nobody seemed to understand or care about these details, a part of the crowd drifted away to a café on the edge of the park. Then the second fat man began to speak, and I thought: here we go. He called on the people of Budapest to rise against their oppressors, to drench the city in the blood of the oppressors, to close the factories and schools now, tonight, with their united strength. The men who had gone to the café came back, and the police looked interested; one of them began rapidly taking notes. Toward the end of his oration, the speaker began pointing to one section of the plaza, then another, as if there were masses of cadres in each, shouting orders—you, the workers of the ironworks, go here tonight in the city; you, the peasant revolutionaries, go to the farm of Koacs (a

local truck farmer who sold radishes of immense size)—
pointing to these invisible cadres and becoming hoarse in
the throat with the effort of organizing this revolution
which would be all over in a night's work. The people in
the square looked puzzled, then rather miffed, that this
man had so puffed up their ardor and then turned out to
be crazed. The police, however, were more interested
than ever, taking notes, and obviously making prepara-
tions for their own defenses against this plan they
were hearing, miraculously, for free. The crowd drifted
away again, and by the time the orator had finished, I
would say there were no more than ten of us remaining,
all a little dazed.

Adolescence is a truly dreadful phase of life. A person
is free, and unarmed to deal with freedom. We tell the
young, "My dears, you are young, everything is possible,
how we envy you." They, poor things, know that it is no
very big step from possibility to disaster; yet they have
no weight of years to keep them from walking. They are
confused and afraid, as they should be, by this freedom.
So that what we witness is their search to find a realm of
life in which they can immediately belong. I certainly
wanted to belong to the invisible cadres at the mass rally.
I did not so much disbelieve the fiery speaker as wish that
the vast audience he imagined was actually there. This
is what the famous "search for identity" among the young
consists of: the longing for a group or a way of life to
glide into, to lose oneself in, and so avoid the terrifying
solitude of liberty. I have seen it happen to my students.
Young people should not spend the years from twenty
to thirty in libraries, taking notes in classrooms, perform-

The Frog Who Dared to Croak

ing for us; they have done so since the age of five. They should take a break, even if they intend to become scholars, and even if the break is only for a year or two. Travel to Paris, learn the guitar. But no, they cling to their classrooms as to a lifeline.

This excursion does illuminate my own story. My elective affinities began with my working-class lovers; they continued among my working-class comrades. But this led to no peace for me. My comrades were miserable, and beginning to revolt. I found a home among them in these struggles more truly home than the rooms of our comfortable, secure house, but in this new home there was anger and hatred against the world. Hatred of the world as it is: the noblest emotion an adolescent can feel. Unfortunately, I was poorly fitted for the role of adolescent rebel.

The sight of blood made me ill. I sought excitement but feared violation at the same time. I did fight back against my attacker in the park, but it was spontaneous; for nights after I relived the scene in my dreams, not as the triumphant David, but lying on the ground helpless to ward off kicks. I do not know if one could call me a coward. My adventures in the park were all about danger resolved, the statues turning into warm bodies. Against the class enemies of my lovers, my imagination ran riot with acts of violence. I imagined that the police forced me to drink blood and that I choked on it; I dreamed that someone kicked me and that I deflated like a punctured balloon. So I was a youth half armed for the "historical role," as we like to say, to which my sympathies led me. My imagination made me a weak comrade.

This, gentlemen, was the condition in which I entered our glorious movement.

6

The materials Grau labeled "6" consist of a police file and a letter from Tibor Grau's father to his aunt. The text makes clear how the police file came into the elder Grau's possession. I may perhaps be permitted a surmise as to how both documents came into the possession of the son. The Grau family, as the elder Grau's letter makes clear, maintained a bank vault in Zurich. Both the police file and the letter were deposited there. The younger Grau must have come into custody of this bank vault upon his father's death. An inquiry I made to the Swiss Cultural Mission in London produced, of course, a total refusal to explore, or even to discuss, the matter. But "6" shows physically no traces of being hidden, nor does the preceding "5" or some of the later documents, written after the Second World War. I surmise that once Grau returned to Hungary after the Second World War, he was able to make use of this vault from time to time to store his papers.

Dossier   Department of Royal Security
              Juvenile Division, Budapest Section
              Surveillance and Interrogation Report
              Subject: Tibor von Grau
              Code file: SS JD BS 19998
              Previous code file: none
              Date of code file: June 26, 1913

Subject Summary: Born Sept. 1, 1893, son of Herbert von Grau and Emma Weiss (no cross-reference file). H. von

The Frog Who Dared to Croak

Grau knighted 1887. Parental religion: H. von Grau and E. von Grau, Jews. Parental occupation: H. von Grau, banker. E. von Grau, deceased, 1895. Other adult relations in household: Doreen Weiss, maternal aunt.

Subject Educational History: Tibor von Grau admitted to St. Stephan's School 1900, graduated with highest honors 1910, admitted to Budapest University 1911. Student of philosophy. Excused from military service Dec. 1, 1911.

Physical Characteristics: Ht., 1 meter 73 cent.; weight, 62 kilo. Eyes, blue; lips, full; nose, straight, high bridge; hair, brown; complexion, light, face heavily pitted by acne scars. No glasses, no visible deformities.

Instigation of Surveillance: Complaint by F. Borodin, Asst. Keeper of Kaiser Library (attached). Complaint alleges T. Grau with fomenting revolutionary discussions among a group of students working in philosophy section of library. Staff meeting March 16: complaint reviewed, classified C-status, Detective Sergeant Bruck assigned for intermittent surveillance. Surveillance dates: March 21, 27; April 3–8, April 11, April 15 (Lassalle Rally—see cross-reference 19213).

Action: Complaint reduced to F-status; subject put on monthly report, file closed Nov. 16, 1913.

Narrative Report (filed April 17, Detective Sergeant Frederick Bruck, badge JD-17): On March 21, I went to Kaiser Library and identified myself to F. Borodin, Asst. Keeper (see attached complaint). He provided me with a pass, identifying me as private secretary to a retired professor of philosophy at the university. In order for this cover to be effective, I ordered Borodin to inform no one else on the library staff of my identity.

First Steps

I then proceeded to the philosophy section of the library. I had been given a small booth consisting of chair, desk, and bookshelf—called a "carrel"—in a room ringed by forty such carrels. In the center was a long table used by younger university students. It was easy to observe anyone at the table from my carrel; usually the subject von Grau took a chair at the table directly opposite me.

Effective cover required that I appear to be studying. I had asked F. Borodin for a suitable text to read, owing to my unfamiliarity with the field. He suggested a work by Immanuel Kant (*Critique of Judgment*). I also took the liberty of procuring some other books, whose titles seemed less forbidding and so would make access to the young von Grau easier in striking up a conversation. These titles played more of a role in the investigation than anticipated: *Masterworks of Prussian Thought*, edited by Otto von Stumpf; *The Secret Life of Martin Luther*, by Ernst Mayr, and a title translated from the French, *Philosophy of the Inner Room*, by the Margrave von Sade. Having assembled these works, and having ascertained the plan of exits, toilets, and bookstacks in the philosophy section, I concluded work for the day.

One week later, on March 27, I returned to the Kaiser Library to begin a period of sustained surveillance. As soon as I sat down at my carrel, I perceived something was wrong. All eyes at the long table were on me; a few heads popped out of other carrels to stare. I noticed that the four books were not in the same order in which I had left them on the desk. To regain cover, I picked up the book on top, by Margrave von Sade, took out a pen and notebook, and made it appear I was studiously taking notes. I happened to glance at the text, and immediately perceived my error. This book is a piece of pornography, such as we seized from that bookshop in the Budhalle last December 17. The philosophers, who for the most part look anemic, obviously thought me a sex maniac. I quickly put down the Margrave von Sade, took up *The Secret Life of Martin Luther*, in content altogether harmless, totally uninteresting. Subject von Grau entered the library about a half hour later. Like the others, he stared.

At eleven in the morning, it is customary for the scholars in the philosophy section to take coffee together in the basement of the library. An elderly man came over to invite me to participate. I agreed, as it would provide the first direct contact with the subject.

In the basement, a remarkably elegant samovar and coffee set—a gift, I later learned, from the subject's father. Asked by a man of my own age what brought me to the library, I explained that I was engaged in some private research, not connected with the affairs of the retired professor of philosophy. A silence. Someone else then said, "I happened to glance at the books you are reading. It's a rather . . . unusual collection. What sort of research exactly are you engaged in?" Naturally, I had prepared for this question—but before realizing the exact character of the von Sade book. However, there was nothing for it. I had to go ahead. I replied, "I am studying the relation between Luther, Sade, and German political thought." Reply produced an almost magical, totally unexpected effect. People crowded round, smiling appreciatively, nodding at each other. I heard one man remark to von Grau, "Obviously a project of genius. Why have we never known of him before?" Von Grau himself looked at me with something of the expression of a happy dog greeting its master.

I give all these details to explain how I so quickly not

only established contact with the subject but was received immediately as a member of the circle.

The Budapest Circle, as this group had come to be known, is certainly conspiratorial in manner and subversive in thought. However, they are harmless. They like to talk, and are happiest gathered round the silver samovar in the library, arguing about what the country should be like after the revolution. How the revolution will occur is, in the words of one of them, "simply a consequence of historical necessity." The complainant has been led to overemphasize the danger of the Budapest Circle because he takes too seriously certain words. "All this talk and no action!" one of the circle will suddenly cry. "Now is the moment to go into the streets, to create history, to incite the revolution!" The others will fall silent when such a speech is made; they become ashamed and stare at their hands. But no one leaves the library.

Following this initial success, I was able to conduct surveillance of the subject more easily and more directly. From April 3 to 7, I would arrive at the library at around ten in the morning; he would usually arrive around 10:30. He would work until the coffee hour, spend perhaps forty-five minutes in social conversation, then return to work at the long table without interruption until four in the afternoon, when he would leave to attend philosophy lectures at the university. The boy is an intense worker. He sits for hours at a time reading, the book held in both hands before him. He appears to read an entire chapter and then to write notes about it. He does not eat lunch.

On April 3, I was able to speak for ten minutes with the subject during the coffee break. He asked if Martin Luther more resembled Justine or Juliette. This reference being obscure, I "returned the serve" by asking him what he thought. He replied at length. I did not at first understand it; when I did, I wished I had never asked the question.

Von Grau talks mostly about very abstract matters, however. He does not read the newspapers regularly, and is not well-informed about politics. In these four days, I have heard him mention political subjects twice, and with scant interest. He wants mostly to talk about the relation between philosophy and drama.

Nor is the subject popular. Within the Budapest Circle, he has only two friends, Bruno and Maria (last names indeterminate; male approx. 20, thin, frail, and lethargic; female ditto). Like von Grau, they have at most a moderate interest in politics. The other members of the circle are afraid of him. If he is challenged, as he was during the third day of sustained surveillance by a man named Otto (last name indeterminate, approx. 25, medium height and weight, face no distinguishing marks), he becomes aggressive. The subject and Otto talked about some sort of distinction between being and action; von Grau kept hammering at the arguments of Otto until not only were they destroyed but the man humiliated. Most important fact to emerge about subject's character: he is lonely.

As of April 7, I would have recommended reducing matter to F-status, and discontinuing surveillance. Two events kept inquiry active. On April 8, I received a note in library box from subject, inviting me to meet outside library the afternoon of April 11. Second, a chance remark made by Bruno on the same day that he, Maria, and subject would attend the Lassalle Rally a week later.

The meeting on April 11 perhaps does not belong in an official report, as it contributed nothing toward determination of the subversion status of the subject. However, it does cast some light on one significant aspect of the subject's subsequent behavior at the Lassalle Rally.

The meeting was at 6, closing time at the library. I walked out of the building to find subject pacing back and forth at the bottom of steps. Asked where we should go. He suggested a walk in the Municipal Park. I found this odd, as it was dark and drizzling. Accepted. We walked to the park in silence.

At the entrance to park we met Patrolman Hertz. In contravention of established procedure, Hertz (Badge PD-6) said, "Good evening, sir." Von Grau was surprised. He said, "Do you often come here, then, Fritz?" I covered over by saying Hertz had worked for my father. Von Grau asked what my father did. I said he was a tin dealer. For some reason, subject made this comment: "I also would like to work with my hands. It would be such a relief to . . . and then there are times when I feel I am going to burst. I have had headaches . . . that's what I would like, hard work, and to see other people . . . sort of meld in." Perhaps the words "tin dealer" set his mind on melting in.

We walked into the wooded part of park. I thought perhaps a secret was going to be disclosed. But the subject simply repeated the question, "Do you ever come here, Fritz?" When I said no, von Grau said, "I thought not." We walked in silence again to the other gate, and went to the café at the corner.

Von Grau began asking many details about my life. Following procedure, I told the truth insofar as it did not give me away. I had to invent a university career at Tübingen, but Grau seemed to believe me. In any event, he was more interested in whether I had played sports, which ones, etc. Did I like to swim, to hike, etc. At end of coffee, subject said he would like to see me again and asked for my address. I said I was in process of changing houses, and that the library was the best place to meet. "I'll count on that," he said, and left.

At the April 14 meeting of our unit, it was decided that I should attend the Lassalle Rally the next day. PD squads were alerted to make sure Hertz mistake not repeated. I have said in official minutes before, and I will say again, that the importance of this annual rally is in certain quarters overestimated. The only arrests the juvenile unit had made in the years before were for drunkenness. A large police presence serves as a provocation. The unfortunate events at this year's rally were entirely accidental. Had Colonel Schramm's horse not fallen, it would simply have been more of the same. No significance can be attached to my presence; I was rounding out a routine inquiry.

Squad 5 will file the Disorderly Disturbance and Arrest forms in due course. I can only contribute a report as to how events looked from the crowd.

I met the subject, Bruno, and Maria at the library, as we had arranged, at 11:00. Von Grau and Bruno were deep in discussion about stage plays, from the library until we came to the square itself. They were hardly conscious of their surroundings, and their position near Colonel Schramm was therefore purely accidental. The four of us were on the southeast corner of the square, in front of the bakery. During the singing of the songs, which began the rally, approximately twenty people separated us from Colonel Schramm. When the speeches then began, the crowd surging in from the southeast corner pushed us to within three meters of him, with still the twenty people packed in between. Colonel Schramm's horse was pushed from our side. I saw him suddenly topple from his saddle; no hands pulled him down, he looked simply as if he had lost his mount. The horse, frightened by the swirling crowd, began to rear up. The crowd between us and Colonel Shcramm had shied away from him in panic. Thus I saw clearly that it was the horse which stepped on Colonel Schramm's calf. As he has reported, in the agony of the moment, he imagined a person had struck him. He drew his pistol. I ran toward him, crying out, "Schramm, it's me, Bruck!" He dazed with pain, fired at me. The shot sent people around me into a panic, his horse now bucking and rearing out of control. There was blood from Schramm's wound flowing onto the ground.

I stopped momentarily when Schramm fired. Von Grau ran around me at that point, yelling, "Run, Fritz, run!" He ran toward Schramm. Schramm fainted from pain, the gun fell out of his hand. Just after the gun hit the ground, von Grau reached him and kicked him in the side. At this moment, the detail commanded by Corporal Nagy broke through the panicking crowd; one patrolman grabbed the reins of the horse, and two others seized von Grau.

Corporal Nagy, at the back of his detail, recognized me. Following Disorderly Disturbance and Arrest procedure, I directed Nagy to take Bruno and Maria into custody as associates of a suspect present at scene of arrest. I absolutely confirm Corporal Nagy's report that he did so in an orderly and, given the circumstances, considerate manner. Discipline was observed by the entire detail. The trouble was the number of other details that converged on the scene in the wake of this initial one. The crowd to the south of us, seeing approximately fifteen uniformed policemen leading off three adolescents, and having had no clear view of the events preceding, and the young von Grau being smeared with blood on the knees of his trousers, from having slipped in Colonel Schramm's gore after kicking him, the crowd imagined von Grau to have been beaten by this mass of policemen and became hostile. Again, I absolutely confirm that the men of all details acted with impeccable discipline under severe provocation.

Interrogation Report: The subject and two associates were brought to the central interrogation unit at 12:45: Tibor von Grau (see top of this file); Bruno Schwart, Maria Piset (see appendix for associate identification cards; they are the Bruno and Maria of indeterminate last names in the surveillance report above). Associates held for brief questioning; negative information; released without restriction.

The potential charge against the subject was assault of a police officer while performing duty (section 4-ODPO-2 of Juvenile Justice Code). Subject was held from 12:45 until 15:45 without interrogation, pending statement from Colonel Schramm. Verbal statement taken from Colonel Schramm at 15:00. Colonel Schramm confirmed my verbal report that subject had acted spontaneously, believing he was protecting me. Preliminary opinion of Prosecutor's unit is that case could be difficult, as von Grau was in fact protecting one policeman against weapon attack from another. Unit conference at 15:30 decided on routine interrogation procedure for juveniles, with hidden stenographer, and no charges to be preferred unless warranted by interrogation process itself. Also, in accordance with procedures governing influential families, the father of von Grau was notified at approximately 16:00 of his son's detention. The relevant portions of the interview transcription are:

INTERROGATOR (Sergeant Bruck): You must be surprised to see me here.

SUBJECT (Tibor von Grau): You mean you were . . . all along . . .

INTERR.: Yes.

(Lack of response)

INTERR.: Do you know why I was there, at the library?

SUBJ.: No.

INTERR.: Someone at the library had filed a complaint about you—

SUBJ.: Who was it? Bruno?

INTERR.: Why should it be Bruno?

SUBJ.: (*pause*) . . . I don't know, I've not had anything to do with anyone else from school.

INTERR.: I'm not allowed to say where the complaint came from. But I can tell you what it was about. It concerned your statements and behavior.

SUBJ.: But I've never done anything there. I never would. Did you know this when we went to the park . . . of course you would . . . but you told me so much about yourself . . . it was a trap . . .

INTERR.: Now, Tibor, that's not quite fair. We never discussed politics, did we?

SUBJ.: Politics, no: so what?

INTERR.: Well, Tibor, I don't know you well enough yet to say whether—

SUBJ.: What did you say, my political activities?

INTERR.: Yes.

SUBJ.: And that's why you were spying on me?

INTERR.: It's not spying. I'm a public official. I have to protect the public when its interests are threatened; that's my job.

SUBJ.: And that's what you thought about me?

INTERR.: Yes.

(No response)

INTERR.: Now, what could you have done to cause this complaint?

(Lack of response)

INTERR.: We can come back to this. About today. I appreciated what you did for me; it was very brave.

(No response)

INTERR.: You do understand, don't you, brave as you were, we have a problem. You assaulted a police officer, and you are suspected of having dangerous political tendencies. This is serious.

(No response)

INTERR.: Now, this won't do. If you will help me, we can clear these matters up together. If you keep silent, what am I to think?

(No response)

INTERR.: This is not good. I'm going to leave you alone for a few minutes, and I want you to think very seriously about what you can tell me about the complaint we have had of you. I'll leave you in this room; a man will be outside the door. Knock on the door if you want to use the toilet, or if you would like some water. The door is locked. I'll come back whenever you want me.

The interview concluded at approximately 16:05. Ten minutes later, the guard opened the door on routine check. The subject was still in his chair, but rocking slightly back and forth. This is a familiar hysterical symptom, and I went to the guardroom to ask one of the men to come in to assist me. It can be the sign that a subject will soon become violent. But the rocking continued unchanged. The guard moved to hold von Grau by the shoulders, but I motioned him away. After this rocking had continued a few minutes longer, I called in the duty doctor for the day. His opinion was that some kind of catatonic crisis was underway.

While we were considering our next move, Margrave von Grau arrived at the police interrogation unit (approx. 16:30). He not unreasonably demanded immediate custody of the boy, assuming no formal charges were to be filed against him. In view of this request, a short conference was held among myself, the duty doctor, Chief Inspector Bolz, and the representative of the Public Prosecutor. I recommended no charges be filed. The duty doctor reported on the alarming state of the subject's health. The difficulty, as always, was the press. To let this young man go would possibly give the appearance of being swayed by his family's standing, rather than by humanitarian motives and an absence of compelling security reasons to keep him. We determined, therefore, on report-release. The father, in taking custody of the subject, has signed the two-week report form, so that for the next six months we shall have fortnightly accounts of the young man, certified by his legal parent.

Unit Summary: Surveillance and Interrogation reports of Detective Bruck certified for records of Juvenile Division at unit meeting, April 21. Consensus that the initial C-status was too high for the case. General discussion of better classification procedures in future. Minutes drafted to Chief Inspector G. Bolz, recommending that complaints of a political nature made by individuals, based on direct observation, require confirmation by a second party before being accorded C-status. General discussion of breaking cover during surveillance. No recommendation made. General discussion of Public Prosecutor intervention in Juvenile Division cases before interrogation completed. No recommendation made. Review recommended of arrests at Budhalle Exotic Bookshop (file SS O 18886) to determine what relation, if any, to library personnel. Detective Bruck detailed to review of subject's custody report forms.

April 15, 1913
Willow House, Budapest 7

Dear Agnes,

I am having Gyorgÿ deliver this to you by hand, for reasons that will become all too evident. Briefly, Tibor was arrested by the police today; I have taken him home in custody; he has had a brainstorm, and is now under sedation. The doctors, who have just left the house, believe he will regain his faculties in several days, but will require weeks to recover fully. Obviously, you will want to come back to town immediately. Tell the servants that they will remain on full pay. I think we should bring Tibor to the country to recuperate as soon as he is fit to travel.

I will try, my dear, to tell you everything I know about this terrible crisis, but I know little, and I am so disturbed in myself that what I do know I may not well relate. Please bear with me. This afternoon a policeman came to the bank to tell me Tibor was in custody. I had a premonition it had something to do with violence that broke out at the Lassalle Rally—this is a socialist gathering that the police, for reasons I do not understand, permit to occur each year—but the man who came to fetch me would tell me nothing. I arrived at the police station, identified myself, and was told Tibor was "temporarily unavailable." You may imagine how I received this. I gave Gyorgÿ, who accompanied me, a note for the Assistant Commissioner of Police—you may remember this man, we had him once to tea with his wife, the English lady. The Assistant Commissioner arrived in the waiting room in about ten minutes, I will say that for him. He was suitably responsive and disappeared to find Tibor. Another ten minutes and he returned to say that the difficulty was medical rather than legal. I thought they had tortured my boy! I began to demand immediate action, and a Detective Sergeant Bruck was shown into the room. He told me the following: on advice of an anonymous tip, he (Bruck) had had Tibor under surveillance for the last few weeks. Evidently, his fellow students at the philosophy library indulge in all sorts of wild talk, as young people will, and some fool had taken them for genuine revolutionaries. There is no question, Bruck told me, of any substance to these accusations of subversive thought as they concern Tibor. I suppose this means he thinks there is some substance to the suspicions against the others. In any event, the Budapest Circle—that is what these young people call themselves—decided to go to the Lassalle Rally. Something about a horse and a wounded policeman I couldn't make out, but anyhow Tibor tangled with a policeman who had threatened someone else. Does the name Fritz mean anything to you? I've never heard

The Frog Who Dared to Croak

Tibor talk about his chums at the library. There is no question of a charge; evidently, there was such violence that many people, police as well as youngsters, were over-excited.

The problem seems to be that the shock of being arrested has caused a brainstorm in Tibor. I was taken in to see him. He was rocking back and forth, silently. Agnes, I will never forget the sight of him rocking, staring. I called out to him. He recognized me. I signed a form taking custody of him, and brought him back in the carriage.

I had Gyorgÿ bring Dr. Kramer to the house. He arrived just a moment after our carriage. At home, Tibor stopped rocking. Dr. Kramer sent me out of the room, but I refused to go. I can therefore tell you something of the problem, though I will not try your nerves with a complete account. He does respond when a light is held up to his eyes, by turning away. This is evidently a good sign. Moreover, he responds to loud sounds in the ears. He responds to a hammer on the knee. His fingers are not tensed, evidently another good sign. Dr. Kramer gave him an injection to make him sleep. A nurse is on duty outside his room constantly.

I will of course make sure, through the Assistant Commissioner, that his dossier is removed from the official files and given to me. I do not think I shall have to pay to do this; I believe it will be done as a favor, and in recognition of the harm such a document could do one of our standing . . .

I'm sorry, Agnes, exhaustion has overtaken me, and I fell asleep for several hours. It is now early morning. I have been to Tibor's room. He is sleeping soundly, which the nurse says is a good sign. We are so seldom done in

First Steps

by the desire to commit a colossal folly, especially when we are young. Disaster comes from a small stumble to the side. I don't know for you, my dear, but when I look back at my own life, it was the little thing that always snared me; a glance returned at the theater, which set in motion a great misunderstanding; one sharp word to an employee, which made him my secret enemy forever after. Tibor has taken such a stumble to the side, though why the punishment is to his own wits, I do not understand.

You and I have done the best we can for him. Do you remember telling me once his imagination frightened you? I did not see at the time, but perhaps this sort of thing is what you meant . . . We have done our best, or perhaps you have. I know I was not always successful in beating down anger that came to me when he refused to be normal, to play games or play with his toys, going instead to his room to dream. I have seen so many grow confused, become vulnerable, under the sway of their sensibility. Even though it was a miracle that our boy became so physically strong, I have always feared for him.

Come home.

Nicky

Part Two

Grau's First
Revolution

The Soviet Hungarian Republic was established on March 22, 1919. It lasted until August of 1919, when a Rumanian army invaded the country and captured Budapest. The revolutionary regime was a child of the First World War. When the Hapsburg empire broke up, Hungary, like its neighbors, was plunged into chaos. The ethnic groups in the country—Magyars, Rumanians, Teutons—were hostile to each other; the economy collapsed. This chaos gave radical elements in Budapest, aided by the new Russian regime, their chance; they seized power in the name of a "people" unhappy with itself.

The very chaos which made the Soviet Hungarian Republic possible also doomed the regime to fail. Many in the country were surprised it was able to last even four months. In addition to the social and economic problems of the country, the regime was beset by fights among its leaders. The Foreign Minister, Béla Kun, was a revolutionary trained by Russian Bolsheviks; he sought to bring the Hungarians under Russia's control, and others in the government resisted him. Those who believed in the dictatorship of the proletariat battled those who believed in social democracy. There were too many official posts, since the Imperial regime rewarded the faithful by creat-

*ing work for them in an ever more elaborate govern-
mental maze. Official duties frequently overlapped. Tibor
Grau was one of those who worked in this bureaucracy
in which new men did old jobs, or old men discovered
they had been engineers of the Revolution all along.*

*Each of these documents is in an excellent state of
preservation, further supporting my surmise in the note
to "6." Here, numbers "7" through "10" are written in
Hungarian, and "11" is in German.*

7

Department of Official Announcements
Office of the Deputy Director

April 1, 1919

Dear Tibor,

We have a little problem here about which I'd like to
consult you. The Department of Official Announcements
commissioned a poem two months ago from Stepan Worz,
the writer who was so helpful to us during the early days
of the Revolution. We want to use the official poem on
various public occasions, as well as to print it in the
newspapers after the more routine announcements from
our ministry—sort of spiritual uplift, you know? Well,
Worz wrote the poem, but there's something wrong with
it, even though it celebrates the glory of the department's
mission. We'd like your help in making it more suitable.
Here is the poem:

Words, words, and words. What else, when men are dead,
Their small lives ended and their saying said,

Grau's First Revolution

Is left of them? Their children go to dust,
As also their children's children must,
And their belongings are of paltry worth
Against the insatiable consuming earth . . .
I knew a man and almost had forgot
The wisdom of the letters that he wrote;
But words, if words are wise, go on and on
To make a longer note of unison
With man and man than living persons make
With one another for whatever's sake.
Therefore, I wept tonight when quick words rose
Out of a dead man's grave, whom no one knows.

I would be grateful for any suggestions you might have in
rescuing this poem.

　　　　　　　　　　　With best wishes,
　　　　　　　　　　　André Birn

Department of Cultural Propaganda
Office of the Deputy Director
　　　　　　　　　　　　　　　　April 2, 1919

Dear André,
　　Thanks for your letter of April 1 about the Worz
poem. I do think there are some few things that we might
do to make the poem better. From the point of view of
correct ideology, line 6 must be changed. "The insatiable
consuming earth" is a despondent image, implying that
the achievements of socialism mean no more than the
vain strivings after gain under the old order. In fact,
Worz seems well aware of this, since in the previous line
he says people's "belongings are of paltry worth." I propose, therefore, the sixth line to read: "Against history's

consuming work . . ." The rhyme is a little off, but the sense is better:

> And their belongings are of paltry worth
> Against history's consuming work . . .

Now, line 12 is another ideological misstep. Here Worz uses the phrase "for whatever's sake," implying words could be greater than revolutionary deeds, and again striking the pessimistic note. This is easily corrected: substitute "that" for "than" in line 11, and use in the next line "in socialism's wake." Thus, you get the lines:

> But words, if words are wise, go on and on
> To make a longer note of unison
> With man and man that living persons make
> With one another in socialism's wake.

These changes should do the trick.

> Best wishes,
> Tibor

Department of Official Announcements
Office of the Deputy Director

April 4, 1919

Dear Tibor,

Thanks so much for the Worz poem suggestions. I know how busy you are, and I hesitate to impose on you any further, but since you've helped us this much, could you just take us a bit further with the revisions, as we are still a little unhappy with the poem, from the vantage point of its propaganda use. The lines in the middle:

Grau's First Revolution

> I knew a man and almost had forgot
> The wisdom of the letters that he wrote

seem to us here at the department a bit obscure, but perhaps they could be reworked to give a better introduction to your very excellent image toward the end of the poem. Also the last two lines:

> Therefore, I wept tonight when quick words rose
> Out of a dead man's grave, whom no one knows.

The image of the ordinary and unsung person as poet is of course great. But what do we do about the "Therefore," since "in socialism's wake" precedes it in the new version; and why does the writer weep, since now, thanks to you, he is being led forward by socialism? You see the literary problem; it's beyond us.

> Best wishes,
> André

Department of Cultural Propaganda
Office of the Deputy Director

April 5, 1919

Dear André,

Well, we are in deep water indeed. Given the complexity of the problem, I've consulted with some other people on my staff; I think that our collective wisdom may have produced a solution. You are perfectly right, a man can't be allowed to weep in the wake of socialist progress. And the earlier lines you refer to do seem to us, also, to be obscure.

Let's deal with the obscurity first, since this sort of problem is usually the easiest to clear up in poems. We've

The Frog Who Dared to Croak

finally decided that the best thing to do is simply to deform the rhythm a bit for the sake of giving the lines sense. We suggest the following change:

> I knew a man named Marx, and almost had forgot
> The wisdom of the letters that he wrote

Now the big problem, the last two lines: we think you and your colleagues have a choice. The last lines could read:

> Therefore, I cried tonight when strong words rose
> Out of a dead man's grave, whom no one knows.

This is uplifting, but it has the unfortunate religious suggestion that there is life after death, a superstition which is officially banned. The other possibility:

> Therefore, I cried to read the strong words which rose
> From a dead man's tombstone, whom no one knows.

Here everything is correct ideologically, and the rhythm is balanced. Unfortunately, there is a slight grammatical confusion about the word "whom," but we think it would be prissy to object to the solution on these mechanical grounds, and suggest you opt for this second ending. Here is the entire poem in the revised form:

Words, words, and words! What else, when men are dead,
Their small lives ended and their sayings said,
Is left of them? Their children go to dust,
As also all their children's children must,
And their belongings are of paltry worth
Against history's consuming work . . .
I knew a man named Marx, and almost had forgot
The wisdom of the letters that he wrote;

Grau's First Revolution

But words, if words are wise, go on and on
To make a longer note of unison
With man and man that living persons make
With one another in socialism's wake.
Therefore, I cried to read the strong words which rose
From a dead man's tombstone, whom no one knows.

   Happy official announcing!
                              Tibor

8

                              Budapest
                              April 20, 1919

Dear Father,
   I hope you are enjoying Zurich, and that the nursing
home is taking good care of Aunt Doreen. There is still
nothing possible to be done about your return to Budapest.
I saw the Minister as soon as I returned yesterday. He
says you must wait; the bank's affairs are still being
audited by the revolutionary accountants. Until this is
completed, and it is certain who among your clients has
taken money abroad, and how much, nothing can be done.
The Minister must seize whatever assets of your clients
remain in Hungary, to approximately the amount taken
abroad. My understanding with him about your personal
account remains firm.
   Manfred is delivering this letter by hand to you, along
with a sealed package. *Do not open this package!* I say so
for your own protection. Put the package in our safe-
deposit vault in the Zurich bank. If ever I need it with-

drawn, Manfred or someone else will ask you for "St. Theresa." Please memorize this sign, as I expect you to destroy this, like all my other private letters. I will be writing you openly by the post soon. Give Aunt Doreen a kiss for me.

Je t'embrasse
Tibor

Cjur Revolutionary Journal   April 13, 1919

MASSACRE IN WOODS

The bodies of two men were found yesterday morning in the Cjur woods, about six miles from town. The men had been shot, police believe, with a small-caliber revolver; the wounds on the deceased indicate they were shot at close range. Police speculate they were blindfolded and then slain, although no blindfolds were found near the bodies. These are the only details made available at this time. The police indicate, however, that the men were neither of our town nor of our province, but come from Budapest.

Cjur Revolutionary Journal   April 14, 1919

CULTURE AND THE PEASANT

Comrade Tibor Grau, Deputy Director of Cultural Propaganda for the Revolutionary Government, honored our little town with a speech last night at the Hall of Peace and Revolution. A dedicated audience listened raptly to his words. Comrade Grau said that the Revolution aims not to "bring culture to the people, but to make the people the culture." He explained these profound words by saying that under the old regime the villagers and peasants were thought too ignorant or stupid to appreciate music and literature. Today we believe that the music of the people, their legends, their history, must become the culture of the country, and that artists and writers must learn from them. Several questions were asked, all of which Comrade Grau answered triumphantly.

Comrade Grau shows promise of great leadership. May we, with all due respect, call attention to his age? He is but twenty-five. Already he has a long and distinguished record of revolutionary activity: he fought with the workers in numerous Lassalle Rallies, and at one he heroically shielded people menaced by a crazed policeman, for which service he was put in jail! Comrade Grau has made other personal sacrifices for the people. He comes from an old, distinguished Budapest family, and is highly educated; yet he has renounced wealth and privilege for the sake of the Revolution. When asked the loutish question at our meeting, "What do you know of the songs and tales of the common people?" this young leader replied, "From my earliest days I have had great sympathy for the workers and peasants. My heart has always belonged to you. And may I say, Comrade Questioner, that it shows no real respect for the people to call them 'common.' It is better said that we are all one."

Due to poor health, Comrade Grau was not able to fight in the Great War. He served his comrades, rather than the Royal masters, during the war, in various ways. After becoming a Doctor of Philosophy in 1915, aged all of twenty-one, this young genius went to work at the war hospital in Budapest, tending the sick. He said to us, "My years of dressing the wounds of soldiers, helping the men learn to walk or to use their arms again, comforting their families if the soldiers were beyond recovery, convinced me that not only must we defeat the capitalist oppressors but we must also dedicate ourselves to a further goal, a world at peace."

Comrade Grau laid particular stress on peace among the various nationalities in our country. When asked, "Are you not basically a Magyar?" this wise young man replied, "We are all human beings." An inspiring reply— and the ideologically correct one. The people, as one people, are great!

Comrade Grau is making a tour of the country this week to bring his message to other villages and towns. Tomorrow he will speak at Zilem, and on April 16 at Verna. It is a pity that his two days among us were disturbed by the terrible events in the woods, but he may be assured that our town is not a haven for murderers. It is the peaceful society of which he dreams the whole world may become the echo!

Cjur Revolutionary Journal   April 16, 1919

SLAIN MEN WERE ENEMIES OF THE PEOPLE

Police released more information today about the two men found murdered in the Tsur woods four days ago. The men carried messages for well-known counterrevolutionary persons in Budapest. Police found these messages in the shoes of one of the slain men. Further, both men wore the so-called Cross of St. Theresa around their necks: readers will recall that the group calling itself the League of St. Theresa consists of bourgeois hooligans bent on destroying the fruits of the Revolution among our people.

Grau's First Revolution

Police speculate that these men were probably shot as a result of some internal warfare within this criminal movement. Anyone with information or knowledge of the events in the Cjur woods is required to come forward immediately.

The lesson of this crime is that, clearly, our enemies have not accepted their defeat at the hands of the people. They still exist, although the very folly of their ways may, as in this case, lead them eventually to destroy one another.

Cjur Revolutionary Journal   April 23, 1919

A YOUNG GIRL'S EVIDENCE

Our readers may recall that eleven days ago two men were found slain in the Cjur woods. From documents on their persons, they were identified as counterrevolutionaries from Budapest. A little more light has now been shed on the mystery by the testimony of Anna Brik, aged 14, daughter of Vremi Brik, our village postman. It tends to confirm the police hypothesis that the counterrevolutionaries were murdered by their fellow traitors.

Anna Brik was delivering a parcel to an outlying farm for her father on April 12 in the late afternoon. She took a shortcut through the woods back to town after making her delivery. She says that she saw across a clearing a car parked in the field of Comrade Brull. Next to it there were four men standing; two of them were blindfolded and had their hands rigidly behind their backs (they were probably bound). The other two men walked freely. She says she also saw two hikers hidden in the woods on the far side of the field, who, like her, were watched by the four men. She said she became afraid, and left as soon and as quietly as possible.

Police say they can confirm at least part of her story. Tape marks were found on the wrists of the two dead men; tire tracks were found in the field near the bodies. However, police found no signs of hikers in the woods. The poor young girl, probably frightened to be alone in the presence of these hooligans, must simply have imagined that there were others to keep her company and keep her safe.

What is clear is that no local people were involved in the murders. Anna says she could not recognize any of the four in the field, nor the two hikers she thinks she saw on the far side of the field. Police find this credible in that Anna, by helping her father with his postal duties, knows everyone in our town and the outlying farms. We are united in defense of the Revolution.

Tour Notes   April 11, 1919

I went with Bruno along a stream in the Cjur woods which comes from caves, hidden springs in the Blauberg which have made caves, or something. I understand nothing of geology. But we walked along the stream, trying to find the cave source, the water lying thin in its bed, cold on the ground. This is my day of vacation before the tour.

Bruno tells me that this day will be "relaxing." I do not feel relaxed. Rather, I am finding that this endless trekking about in uncomfortable boots that have become wet inside opens a gate in my mind. I am overrun with ideas which I can't resist thinking. I am thinking, for instance, about memory: there must be in the brain a huge vault in which even the simplest images are stored, like the image of a foot seen a year ago. This must be so, because such images come back to us unbidden, at any time they choose; we are caught unawares by the memory of something that once was. But how does it happen that an image will suddenly be disinterred from its vault in the brain? Who, as it were, is the curator deciding suddenly to put the picture of the foot on display?

This is not very relaxing for me, since there is no simple answer to the question, "Who is my curator?"

The daylight is almost gone. We have walked twenty kilometers, I believe, since morning.

April 12, 1919

I put down the following because I may need to make use of it someday. If anyone other than me comes to read this, he will find the truth of it attested by Bruno Schwart, who has signed it at the end.

Having reached our destination—a rather small spring coming out of a cave—early this morning, Bruno and I began walking back to the village of Cjur. We calculated that if we walked steadily we could reach the village at dusk. In the middle of the afternoon, we had made better progress than we expected, and decided to walk into the village through a set of fields we had not explored before.

There was a patch of forest between two of these fields. In it, we suddenly saw a car pull up in a cow path in the field ahead of us. Four men got out of the car. Two we could see were bound at the wrists, one of the other two carried a gun. Bruno's instinct was to run forward, but I restrained him; after all, in these times, one never knows. We crept forward.

The light was poor. I could not see the faces of the

men holding the guns—the trees cast them in shadow. But I could see the faces of the bound, and one looked vaguely familiar, although it was hard to tell with the blindfolds. The gunman stepped behind this one and fired into the base of his skull. The second man knelt down, praying for mercy, and the gunman fired into his face.

Bruno and I were stunned. Bruno cried out when the second victim was killed. Either the noise of the report masked his cry, or the assassins were too intent on their task to notice. I pinched Bruno's arm as hard as I could to keep him silent and under control. The assassins took a shoe off each dead man, stuffed a paper into it, then jammed the shoe back onto the foot of each victim. There was horrible gore running out of the heads of the dead men, but the assassins calmly strapped something around the necks of each, wiped their hands on rags, which they threw down beside the bodies, got in the car, and drove off.

Now we ran forward to the bodies. I made sure Bruno did not step in any of the blood. I took off the bandages from the head of the man who looked familiar and, despite the contorted expression, recognized the face. It was Emil Stein, who worked in my department as a writer. I told Bruno to take the bandage off the head of the other; he could not bear to do it, so I did it, but the face was shattered beyond recognition.

Hospital life taught me to overcome physical horror— perhaps that's why I took the job. I thus believe I acted rationally in the circumstances. My immediate thought was that this killing coincided with my visit to Cjur. Bruno was also becoming hysterical, as he will acknowledge. For my own safety as well as Bruno's sanity, I decided to get away from that field as soon as possible, and then keep the affair out of local hands.

We reversed our steps into the woods—thank God it was a dry period—moved from stone to root along the forest for a mile or so, walked along a hedgerow that led to a lane that circles around Cjur, so that we entered the village from the opposite end of the field. We entered Cjur at 19:27. I estimate that the crime took place at approximately 16:00.

Sitting in the mayor's house tonight for dinner, we were interrupted by a policeman near midnight with the news the bodies had been discovered. Bruno and I said nothing; I did ask the mayor that he keep me informed, as a central government official, of whatever he found out, since I had colleagues in the security branch who might assist him if he so desired. He took this to be a plausible request.

For our mutual protection, Bruno and I both now sign this as an accurate account of our experiences this afternoon. This account is being placed in my state-papers bag, so that local authorities can have no access to it, should they try to search us.

April 13, 1919

So it is a plant! Counterrevolutionary documents in the shoe, crucifixes of this so-called League of St. Theresa, which Masur invented. And I, clearly, am the target!

I showed Masur this morning the account that Bruno and I signed. Masur, no fool, intervened yesterday when the report came across his desk that a double murder had occurred in the place where I was vacationing. He came down here secretly last night, reviewed the investigation made by the local police, and issued orders. Evidently, the blunders of the local police are going to make it easier to discover the true nature of this murder discreetly. The yokels walked all over the field and the forest perimeter looking for empty food tins, cigarettes, or other of the usual signs of tramps. The boots of the constables completely obliterated the marks of our own hiking boots. In fairness to them, it should be said they haven't had a murder in Cjur in twenty years, and that automobiles are still a rarity in these parts. Once they noticed the auto marks, they became careless about the rest. (They told Masur, with pride, that they looked for tramp signs "just to be sure.")

Masur seems to believe our account. He told me that Emil Stein has for many years been in the anti-Marxian faction, and that Stein recently wrote an article attacking the offers from our Bolshevik comrades for assistance. I told him such an article was unknown to me, and was, in any case, contrary to departmental regulations about "private" writing. Masur's hypothesis is that the planting of the bogus counterrevolutionary documents and the crucifixes is an attempt to smear the department. Masur believes the murder was timed to coincide with the opening of my provincial speaking tour, in order to cast a shadow over me. This all sounds reasonable.

I must interrupt this record to go give a speech. How I will get through it, I don't know.

April 14, 1919

A crisis was neatly averted today. Evidently, some young girl in the village also witnessed the assassinations, and saw us, though she couldn't see us clearly enough to identify us. Masur put the matter to the mayor this way. If the police credit her story publicly, he will have to issue

Grau's First Revolution

an official reprimand to them for incompetence, since they have obliterated all tracks that would indicate our presence. He said to the mayor: "If you discredit the little girl, I won't discredit you." The mayor is no fool. He has kept Masur's identity under wraps; the police chief (there is a force of three men) is his nephew and hopes to inherit the mayor's house. The mayor simply announced to the chief that the little girl's evidence is on this point to be rejected. The mayor has concocted some neat psychological explanation about the fears of young girls, because undoubtedly the story itself will get around.

Masur's people have a fairly good idea of who the assassins are, and it bears out his initial theory. Sources say two Russians recently entered the country, men known for their work in a revolutionary execution squad. It is also known from different sources that the Education, Cultural Propaganda, and News departments are thought by the Russians to be too liberal and Kerenskyist. This is absurd, but casting the shadow of such a crime over us would justify a change in personnel to a more Bolshevist line. I pointed out to Masur that there was a logical inconsistency in his theory. By committing the murder in Cjur now, these Russians make it seem that I am responsible for the murder, and thus on their side.

My comment made Masur very angry. He said to me, "Tibor, you are a nice boy, in fact, you are a baby. Counter-revolutionaries in your department, a mysterious crime with you in the vicinity, unresolved suspicions: you mix up this stew and you make it necessary for the Revolutionary Council to clean out the department and put in your place a strong man who doesn't let such things happen. They want the stew to stink, they want a mess; a deputy director suspected of murdering one of his people—what could be more perfect? Moreover, my hands are tied. We can't arrest these Russians even if we find them; our guns come from the East. Your only hope is that I can play down the whole thing or create some other crisis to make people forget about this one."

I thanked him. I am also worried about Bruno. Of course, I sent him back to Budapest. He has no head for managing things, and would certainly have given away Masur's presence if he had stayed around. But I've heard nothing at all from him since he left, and he should have signaled me by telegraph, indiscreetly asking for the latest news, as he usually does about anything.

Castle House, Lomitz   April 25, 1919

Dear Tibor,

I'm sorry that I haven't seen you since our vacation, but various family duties have taken me away from the city the last fortnight. The good fellowship we enjoyed on our vacation emboldens me to make a request of you. My father, an inspector of finance in the town of Lomitz, is an able man who, under the monarchy, was unfairly passed over for posts equal to his abilities in the capital. My father graduated from the Imperial Technical school in 1888 with an advanced degree in applied mathematics. He was posted to the general treasury as an underinspector—it was at this time that he came to know your father—and was transferred to Lomitz as inspector of finance in 1895. Normally, such a provincial posting at this rank is a step to moving back to the capital as an inspector after a few years of service. My father, however, never was given this opportunity, and he has passed the last twenty-five years here.

Grau's First Revolution

In the light of our close friendship and our ever-deepening ties, I ask you to intercede on his behalf, if at all possible. I'll write more of a personal nature later in the week.

> Your friend,
> Bruno

Castle House, Lomitz   April 27, 1919

Dear Tibor,

I am disturbed that you haven't replied to my note of two days ago. In case it was lost by the messenger, I'm enclosing my carbon copy. Do please let me know if you can help.

> Your friend,
> Bruno

Castle House, Lomitz   April 30, 1919

Dear Tibor,

Your reply to my letters finally arrived yesterday. Frankly, in the light of all that we have gone through together, I do not think it is an adequate response. Let me point out to you that this is the first time I have ever asked you to assist me. I am by nature an independent man. I am asking nothing for myself, but for my father, the friend of your father. You say, "the Finance Ministry is totally unconnected with my own"; but surely you know people there, you have heard your father speak of those who have had, and who continue to have, influence. And let me remind you that between us there is, if I may put it so, a mutual bond which we have both sworn to

The Frog Who Dared to Croak

observe, and in which to trust one another. If you turn coldly away from me, with this bureaucratic answer, what am I to think? I ask you to reconsider, as a friend and as a companion.

Yours,
Bruno

Cjur Revolutionary Journal   May 5, 1919

THE CRIME EXPLAINED

It's hard to believe that our little town was three weeks ago the scene of a national tragedy, hard to believe that we harbored such a criminal in our midst. In the market-place, outside the Hall of the Revolution, people shake their heads in disbelief and dismay.

Your local newspaper takes pride in having been the first to report the news of the crime. We can claim no role as "sleuths," but we brought you what was known. It is frightening to know that tragedy was so close to our young leader and comrade, Tibor Grau, who spoke eloquently about "Culture and the Peasant." It is heartening that our visitor and comrade has been protected from injury by the security forces of the Revolution, forces founded on the living spirit of justice rather than on narrow, written law.

The editors of the *Cjur Revolutionary Journal* present here a complete record of the crime of Bruno Schwart. Study it well, dear reader: it is a lesson in perfidy that cautions us all to be on guard.

The reader no doubt recalls the events: the traitor Schwart accompanied our comrade Tibor Grau to Cjur. Let the man Schwart tell the next part in his own words

Grau's First Revolution

—we quote from his confession published yesterday. "I arranged a meeting with three other members of the League of St. Theresa for April 12. I abandoned my colleague Tibor Grau in the woods, telling him I wanted to return to our hut to rest. I had surveyed the land where we would vacation, and arranged my meeting with the three league members in the field of farmer Brull. They arrived in a car. Suddenly my confederate Szaz pulled a gun, and announced to me that the two others were in fact high officials of the Security Ministry, reporting directly to the Security Minister, Comrade Masur. We bound their hands, blindfolded them, and executed them. My confederate left in the car, and I returned to the hut, about half an hour before Deputy Director Grau did . . ."

This part of the confession clears up one matter. It is clear that Anna Brik, the postman's daughter, was confused when she said she saw two other men witnessing the execution at the edge of the woods.

At the trial of the traitor Bruno Schwart, which for security reasons was closed to the public, the Minister for Security, Comrade Masur, confirmed another part of Schwart's account. "I am at liberty," he said in the statement of trial proceedings given out to the press, "to reveal that these two of my agents had in fact penetrated into the high councils of the League of St. Theresa. I am also at liberty to reveal," he continued, "that we became suspicious of Schwart when he disappeared from Cjur mysteriously the day after the assassination. Fortunately, the assassins, in their haste and cowardice, fled from the bodies of their victims without searching them. Or were they unable to stomach the very sight of their own villainy? The secret documents left in the shoes of my brave agents have given us further valuable clues. Since

we are on the verge of smashing this counterrevolutionary group, I can reveal no more to the public. But be
assured that these felons will be rounded up shortly!"

The choice of Cjur for a clandestine meeting is
understandable. We are removed from the city and its
bustlings, we are a simple village planted on good rich
soil, enjoying pure air. No one associates us with darkness
and intrigue. Now we know that we must be constantly
on guard. Suspicion is the defense of liberty.

The traitor was, according to the Department of
Official Announcements, shot at dawn this morning.

9

Memorandum to: All members of Department of
Cultural Propaganda

From: Deputy Director T. Grau

Re: Memorandum of April 10, Bureau of Educational
Affairs, Concerning the Teaching of Fairy Tales

Date of this memorandum: May 16, 1919

In my absence, the Bureau of Educational Affairs
published the following edict: "In nursery schools, elementary schools, as well as in educational institutions
standing somewhat higher than elementary schools, for
the edification and amusement of pupils under fourteen
years, there should be recited beautiful and instructive
fairy tales." I participated in the discussions leading to
the drafting of this edict before departing on my tour, and

I am committed to carrying it out in our own department's activities.

While I have been away, I am told, people have been saying that this memorandum is some sort of joke. Those who have said so are foolish; they do not understand that socialist education concerns the whole human being, and must begin at the earliest moment possible. What first fills the heads of children are stories, and we must direct these as we do the subsequent and more intellectual phases of their development. Our department now licenses books; soon it will commission books. In this memo, I want to give you guidelines for both your present and your future work on publications for children.

The earliest ideas of social reality children receive come through folk tales. These tales are also the purest forms of social analysis: the characters are simple, the action makes moral judgments as an inescapable part of the story itself, the tales serve as metaphors rather than refer to other metaphors for their meaning. Theoretically speaking, all propaganda work is thus an elaboration of the *literary form* of the fairy tale.

In the society of the past, the point of most folk tales was to induce the child to accept existing social reality— with the exception of the Robin Hood story, in which the struggle for social justice is presented in terms of a life of crime. In our society, the folk tale must be reshaped to give the child a sense of the reality inherent in social transformation. Let me give you an example of how this can be done.

Most of you were taught the story about the Transylvanian frogs when you were young. In the old story, a family of frogs went on a hopping holiday to the mountains of Transylvania. They encountered strange and

The Frog Who Dared to Croak

frightening animals—wildcats, mountain goats, and wolves. Mamma Frog told everyone to be quiet, not to croak, so that they would escape the attention of these fearsome beasts. But the youngest boy frog was foolishly brave: "I am proud to be a frog," he said, "and it is in the nature of a frog to croak." One day he hopped off on his own, sat beside a mountain pond, and croaked and croaked and croaked, until a mountain goat, attracted by his singing, sprang upon him from behind a tree and ate him up. For days, his father, mother, brothers, and sister searched silently for him. Finally, in despair, they left the mountain. "I told him not to, I told him not to croak," said Mamma Frog. "Do not scold your dead son," said Poppa Frog. "He had the courage to be himself."

Now, this old version is pessimistic, and its meaning is not entirely clear. The socialist version will be as follows:

Once upon a time a band of frogs lived in and around a small pool. It was shady, it had several lily pads, the frogs led an agreeable life. They had some friends, like the colony of snails with whom they frequently dined. They had some acquaintances, like the family of bears who, while lacking much in common with the frogs, were perfectly decent neighbors. One summer, this peaceful existence was threatened. A nest of snakes set up house near the pond. The snakes ate the frogs' lily pads. The frogs moved uneasily around the pond edge, aware that the snakes also wanted to eat *them*.

If the frogs had been united, they could have dealt with the predatory snakes. A frog lacks teeth, but these particular snakes were terrified of noise. Were all the frogs to have bellowed and croaked when they saw a particular frog threatened, they could have driven the snakes away. But the frogs were not united. There were so many lily pads before the snakes set up house at the pond that each frog had one of his own; he thought of it as his property and his alone. So long as his lily pad was safe, each frog did not interfere in what was happening on other lily pads.

There was one frog, older and wiser than the rest, who saw the true nature of the problem, and he had a plan. He proposed that the frogs go camping together, in the Transylvanian mountains. The frogs were so exhausted with worry about the snakes that they were glad to take a week's holiday. They did not know why the older, wiser frog wanted them all to go together, or why he wanted to take them to the mountains, and they did not care. They simply had to get away.

After the older, wiser frog had led them up the mountain, after they had pitched their tents, after the tadpoles had been taken out of their traveling tanks and put to bed in a softly moving stream, the leader spoke to his fellow frogs gathered around the campfire. "My friends," he said, "you see how happy and how safe we are here. Why is it so?"

"Because we have run away," said one frog. "Because there are no snakes," said another.

"No," the older, wiser frog replied. "There are snakes here, there are snakes everywhere; you can't hide from them. What would we do if they attacked us tonight?"

The other frogs became frightened. They glanced to the edge of the clearing. "We would all croak together and frighten them away," one finally replied, and the others nodded agreement.

"Now you see why I have brought you here," said the older, wiser frog. "Why don't you do the same thing in the pond below?"

The Frog Who Dared to Croak

"We are not so stupid as you think," said the first frog who had spoken. "We know we *ought* to croak together, but we have our separate lily pads to protect, and we are afraid of drawing the snakes' attention to our individual places by making noise."

"But you know the whole frog community is in danger?"

"Yes, but each of us hopes that, somehow, he will be left alone if he keeps silent."

"My friends, my dear friends," said the older, wiser frog, "this is exactly the answer I wished to hear. You think you ought to croak, but think it is more 'realistic' to look out for yourselves. Yet just see how dangerous that is. Our comrade is wrong to say you *ought* to croak together; you *must* croak together."

The frogs reflected. There was reason in this speech. They resolved the very next day to return to their ponds, and let off such deafening croaks that the snakes would slither all the way to Paris. But the older, wiser frog spoke once again.

"My friends, if you go off in this mood, you will not have received all the wisdom I wish to impart to you. You will return home, and you will win. You will think my lesson is strength through unity. I mean for you to learn something more. As you were living before tonight, you betrayed each other every time you kept silent. Isn't that shameful! You saw another frog's lily pad eaten, the frog himself menaced, and yet, for the sake of your own pad, you kept silent. What I wish to say to you is this: it is not enough to be strong for a moment. To be strong forever, you must want each other to live. You must treat another frog's life as though it were your own. Imagine that, after having driven out the snakes, you turned on each other, bellowing the weakest off his pad, and then the next weakest, and so on, until only the strongest frog was left, the possessor of all. This would not do. We can defeat the snakes, but we must not become like snakes. To prevent that, we must, I repeat, must treat each other's life as though it were our own. Only through refusing to betray one another will we be strong and happy day after day, week after week, together."

The other frogs did not at first entirely understand this speech. But they talked about it throughout the night, and the more they talked, the more their attitude changed. They offered to exchange lily pads with each other, they offered to share lily pads, finally they decided to treat everyone's lily pad as belonging to everyone else.

It was in this mood of fraternity that they returned home the next day. A snake appeared, hissing at the older, wiser frog himself. He turned to the others in mute appeal. And they croaked; they bellowed until the leaves shook. The bears were amazed; they discovered that, united, the frogs could make as much noise as they themselves, and joining in the fracas, they, too, bellowed. The snails could not shout, but they rattled their shells against each other, and this added to the din. The snake reared up, and fled back to his nest; the noise continued. He and his relatives snatched up their babies, wrapped their pots and pans around their tails, and slithered off into the forest, never to be seen again. The end of the story is: silence reigned in the pond ever after, except for the odd digestive munch or gurgle, or the gentle croak of a frog singing in the bath. Having learned how to be strong, the frogs, thanks to their evening in the Transylvanian mountains, learned also when to exert their strength.

The Frog Who Dared to Croak

Let us analyze what makes this version of the story desirable from a socialist point of view. In three obvious ways, it is acceptable. It portrays the evils of possessive individualism, when the frogs think they separately own their lily pads. It portrays the notion of strength through unity, when the frogs bellow together. And it well illustrates the concept of the revolutionary vanguard, in the effect the united frogs have upon the formerly passive bears and snails. But there is a deeper message built into the story as I have written it, a message about betrayal. Betrayal from within!

Does not the wise old frog counsel the others to know and love one another before they act together? Is not his fear that, having once learned to be strong, they will not know how to be strong? That they will turn on the weaker among themselves, until all are destroyed? I call your attention to a good propaganda use that can be made of this further meaning. We are all of us aware of how much hostility between Magyars, Slovaks, and other groups now threatens the Revolution. This tale could be presented to the young to condition them against harboring such fratricidal emotions. Betrayal from within has got to be uprooted as a human impulse, else suspicion will spread its poison, and our strength will erode.

Let me turn to the major objection that has been raised about this edict—and I recognize it to be a real difficulty. Each of our ethnic groups has its own distinctive folk tales. In the Education Bureau, it was suggested that a representative number of folk stories from each group be presented; this suggestion I believe to be bad propaganda. There will inevitably be a struggle for ethnic hegemony: whose tales are the best made, the most beautiful, and the like, will become questions in which grown men will be reduced to ludicrously infantile discussions in order to maintain the honor of their ethnic origins. Are Slovak bears more courageous than Magyar wolves? And so on.

I have therefore proposed that the ethnic origins of our folk tales be erased, and that we license now, and commission in the future, tales that are told in categorical terms. Fairy tales are going to be indexed under the following headings:

1. Menace of nature to culture: for example, wolves chasing people in a sled, flood stories, bears-in-forest stories
2. Harmony between nature and culture: for example, the story of Miska's three rabbit helpers, the tale of the young boy who helped the muskrats celebrate Christmas (in this latter case, no religious references are allowed—just say, celebrate the winter holidays)
3. Domination relations in culture: here, we will deal with three categories:
   a. Familial domination: for instance, the story of the wicked grandmother and her kind daughters
   b. Political domination: all stories about bad princes, etc.
   c. Domination in relations of production: for instance, the spectacular tale about the five troll bootmakers and their assistants
4. Liberation relations in culture: for instance, the frog-prince stories, Cinderella, etc.

Let me also deal with the suggestion that new stories for children be invented directly from the history of the

The Frog Who Dared to Croak

Revolution itself. This is what our Russian comrades are beginning to do. It is a worthy effort, but I believe it will never be comprehensively effective. The reason lies in the ontological structure of the growth of consciousness (see my pamphlet *Fantasy and Power* for a fuller explanation; I give here only the bare bones, as it were, of the argument). Consciousness develops by the recognition of likeness, then of difference. The young human being appropriates the world by seeing in its animal, cultural, and vegetal variety a unity. The child can feel sorry for a dying plant because he or she can relate it to his or her own living and dying. This appropriation of the world then passes, in the development of the human being, into a recognition of difference. A plant does not die in the same way as a young boy. Finally comes the articulation of the difference between the animal and the cultural. Culture lives and dies beyond the terms of animal feeding, sleep, decay, and death. The moment for fairy tales comes in the first phase. By drawing only on "true" stories from the Revolution, we limit the picture of socialism to but a small area of the unified stage the child sees, on which men, animals, and plants are all of equal value. Thus, by telling only "true" stories, we would leave immense areas of the child's imagination free. The child might believe in our stories of the good socialist child, but he would believe as equally real the old story of the Transylvanian frogs, and this would mean he would consider resignation to be as real as social transformation.

A society which does not possess its people's dreams is not a society in control of itself. I want the young of our country to know *how* to dream. The objection has been raised, we must teach the young only serious and useful things. I answer that there is nothing more serious.

10

Revolutionary Documentation Center
June 1, 1919

Dear Comrade Grau,

All power to the people!

A question has arisen about your police record during the old regime, or rather, several questions. We are writing to ask you to help us resolve matters, if you can.

As you may know, the policy of the Revolutionary Documentation Center has been to preserve all police records from the imperialist regime. The purpose of preservation is twofold. These records contain valuable information on the early phases of revolutionary struggle and the reactions of the Royal police. The old police records also contain information about ordinary felons, the criminally insane, and other deviants who must continue to be of concern to us. The Royal police documentation center separated political, common criminal, and insanity cases, and employed a system of cross-references. You are one of those who are cross-referenced.

The first question that has arisen concerns the fact that your political file is missing. There is simply a note that reads: "All documents transferred to office of Assistant Commissioner of Police." Study of the Assistant Commissioner's files indicates the receipt of the file "SS JD BS 19998 (Tibor Grau)" in the Assistant Commissioner's logbook, and then simply the exit entry of "expedited." For our own records on early revolutionary activity, it would be valuable to know what events or actions caused a file to be created for you; if you happen to have any information on what became of the file, we would also appreciate this datum.

In the section on the criminally insane in the old police records, there is another entry on you that has not been removed, but is cross-referenced to the above political file "SS JD BS 19998 (Tibor Grau)." As is commonly the case in the old cross-referencing system, the political files contain all the factual material, and the psychiatric files contain only medical diagnoses. Your diagnosis in file "C1 B 406" is as follows (only the part relevant to our inquiry included):

> Pronounced neurasthenia, coupled with evidence of Vendome's syndrome. Subject shows reduced response to auditory stimuli, exhibits withdrawal symptom of involuntary rocking. Physical appearance emaciated, despite signs of extensive muscular articulation. Protuberant eyes. Reported history of perversion, despite no anal indication. Prognosis: continued outbreaks of violent hysteria succeeded by catatonic withdrawal, as in present case.

We would like to ask you some rather specific questions about this file; you may be assured that someone in your position can expect the information to be held in confidence. The police surgeon who made this diagnosis, like many employed by the Royal police, had a poor medical education. In particular, he made use of the diagnostic term "Vendome's syndrome," which referred, in the medical schools of the 1860's, to all manner of diseases related to venereal infections. Now, as you know, the Ministry of Health has launched a campaign to rid revolutionary Hungary of these diseases. We have been enlisted to go through old police records and note cases in which Vendome's syndrome appears. It should be said that Victorian doctors, no less prudish than Victorian ladies, grouped under this supposed syndrome various nonvenereal complaints that were linked to sexual activity, like crab lice, or that impaired sexual functioning, like the various vaginal infections. Thus, while we want to assist the new public-health campaign, we are also being rather cautious; we are prepared to spend months making private inquiries before giving the Ministry of Health a list of persons to be interviewed and subjected to treatment. This caution particularly applies to those, like yourself, in official positions.

More importantly, we are also charged with compiling a list of all those suffering from violent hysteria. The security forces then may have an index of persons likely to require hospitalization when confronted with hooliganism or other destructive acts. And again, owing to your position, we are very reluctant to include your name without hearing from you first.

If your political file were not missing, we would probably not be required to bother you at all with these matters, as so often in the capitalist years fighters for freedom were simply treated as insane persons. But owing to this peculiar omission in your dossier, we must pursue these matters in order to put all suspicion to rest.

I will appreciate your comradely cooperation, and the favor of an early response.

Yours,
J. Goldstein

The Frog Who Dared to Croak

Revolutionary Documentation Center
June 5, 1919

Dear Comrade Grau,

Thank you for your letter of June 3. I am delighted that you were able to give me an indication of the political activities that formed the subject of your file "SS JD BS 19998 (Tibor Grau)." In *our* political files, your account has been condensed as follows:

"On April 15, 1913, Comrade Tibor Grau participated in the Lassalle Rally, one of those events in which the tide of socialism surged again forward and higher. Although a young man, he was even then a passionate champion of liberty and justice for the people. At the rally, when *agents provocateurs* caused a few of the people to break discipline, Comrade Grau held firm. It was for this very fortitude that the police of the Royal regime took him into custody. He attempted to restrain a policeman from firing upon a group of the people; he did so by stepping in front of the group, holding his arms out wide, inviting the policeman to fire at him, a statue of calm. The policeman could not—was it not the dawn of some revolutionary sentiment, at least some spirit of fraternity, in his own breast? Comrade Grau was, however, arrested, taken to jail, brutally interrogated, and charged with crimes of perversity and insanity totally opposed to his real conduct. Such was 'justice' under the older order."

Because these accounts of revolutionary activity are likely to be published as inspiring tales someday soon, and in order to keep the historical record on the right course, we have taken the liberty of "smartening up," as they say, your somewhat modest and restrained version.

89

Grau's First Revolution

Nonetheless, between department and department, our problems outlined in my previous letter of June 1 remain. We simply must have from you a statement that indicates:

a. Your ignorance of the whereabouts of your political file, or your knowledge, if you have it
b. Your medical history which bears on the diagnosis of Vendome's syndrome, or does not bear on it, as internally you are already a "marked" name
c. Your medical history which bears on the diagnosis of violent hysteria, as again your name is already marked in official records

All you need to do is send me a letter saying about (a), "I don't know," and about (b) and (c), "I don't have it." Then I can do the paperwork at this end. Thanks again for your help.

Comradely,
J. Goldstein

Dear Comrade Grau,
Thank you for your letter of June 7. I must say that I simply don't understand your attitude. It's not an irrelevant and trivial matter to me; I am not harassing you. This is simply a question of good record-keeping. Just write me a letter of one sentence saying, "I don't know; I don't have it; I don't have it." That's all the Revolutionary Documentation Center wants.

However, if this means so much to you, let me propose a more formal arrangement. We do have a slight problem with which Cultural Propaganda might be able to help.

The Frog Who Dared to Croak

Many of the people detailed to us are somewhat unsuitable. They are academic researchers, who, while undeniably good at unearthing facts in libraries, do not quite understand the nature of our particular mission. They tend to become interested in cases, ferreting out information for its own sake, whether or not the information can be codified according to our guidelines. One of these people, in fact, spotted your case, in the process of conducting a totally useless search for the names of insane persons who had died in prisons rather than hospitals.

Now, I know that Cultural Propaganda is doing research on fairy tales, folk tunes, and the like. Perhaps it would be of interest to you to take our scholars like this man under your wing, so that everyone would feel more comfortable. It is a matter of four people. If they move to you, then I can requisition some proper staff to do their work.

Please let me know.

> Yours,
> J. Goldstein
> June 12

Dear Comrade Grau,

I swear to you it was not my doing. Moreover, I warned you. The violent-hysteria list was sent out of my office by the same idiot who put your name on it. I did not realize you knew Security Director Masur. If you had only told me this, we could have closed the whole file amicably. There was really no need for you to have him personally call me; your own word would have been sufficient. There's something about this I simply don't understand;

however, that doesn't matter. I have my orders, and your file, Comrade Grau, has once again been "expedited."

Yours,
J. Goldstein
Revolutionary
Documentation Center
June 15

11

The following manuscript is handwritten in German.

I have been reading over the many, many documents I kept from those revolutionary days. It is strange to sit quietly in a house, to glance occasionally at the little whitecaps on the Lake of Zurich, and to decide which documents—that is, which memories—one wants to retain. An old man's most valuable possessions are his recollections. Yet, unlike a house, or books, the smaller and fewer of these possessions he has, the happier he is—no, that is not quite right, to weed his memories is to clarify and refine his understanding. Strangely, though I preserved so many weeds, so much from that time, I kept nothing about how this Revolution lasting all of nine weeks ended.

The affair of the documents, you see, was my undoing. I was suspicious of another plot, another betrayal, so I went to my friend, my so-called friend, Security Minister Masur, and out of friendship for me he had a quiet word with Goldstein and then a quiet word with my director.

The result being that I was dismissed the next day, or rather I was informed that I had handed in my resignation to return to academic study. You may well ask why I did not write "I don't know; I don't have it; I don't have it." At the time, I said to myself that I refused because I was afraid to become entangled in the plot being woven around me by making a statement on paper; I was worried they could then produce some other evidence on paper, and I would be proven guilty of lying. But I realize now this explanation does me an injustice. Some stubborn little voice in me was at work, whispering to me probably in my dreams, "No, no, you are free, you don't have to account for your past, you don't need to justify yourself." This voice spoke through me in my refusal, yet at the time I was too cowardly to hear it when I was awake.

So, in any event, my revolution ended before the Revolution. When this larger event occurred, I was, however, as a former revolutionary official, a wanted man. I had to flee Hungary or face jail—certainly not death, I was not so important. Most of the important people went to Moscow. Because of the affair at Cjur, I was neither sure I would be warmly received there, nor was I sure I wanted to go. I decided instead for Vienna.

I say "decided," but this makes it seem a simple matter of getting on the train and leaving. It wasn't. I had to bribe someone at the Office of Passports and Permits for a doctored passport, a suitably worn document with my description and another name. I had to bribe someone else at the Budapest branch of a Viennese bank to transfer funds out of the country. The worst trial was the ludicrous way I escaped from my apartment to the place where I had hidden the documents.

They came for me, you see, one day in the late

morning. I was in the flat below my own, a flat belonging to an actress at the state theater. We heard the counter-revolutionary police, who only two days before were revolutionary police, pounding at my door upstairs.

"Tibor," my actress friend said to me, "you know where to go?" I said I did. "Well then, I shall disguise you perfectly."

She was quite right, it was an artistic disguise. She stuck two tennis balls in my shirt and taped them to my chest (this I found rather painful, as the tape stuck to the chest hairs, so that every time I moved I felt pulling and tugging). She made up my mouth beautifully, tied a babushka around my forehead. She gave me a long, peasant skirt and a blouse, and a frilly shawl for my shoulders. The feet were a problem, but I finally managed to squeeze into some peasant's clogs she had in her wardrobe.

It was dreadful walking with my toes curled over, but I managed to descend the stairs, and to walk past some counterrevolutionary soldiers outside the building (most of them seemed to be from a glass factory near our block of flats). One actually whistled at me, and, I can confess it now, I found this whistle, in the midst of all my danger, rather flattering. In any event, I was free.

My secret flat was half a kilometer away on the same boulevard. The pain of walking in those shoes was unbearable, however, and when I was halfway there, I did something foolish. I stopped at a café where I was known. I simply had to get off my feet, and besides this, I badly wanted a coffee to steady my nerves. The moment I walked in, the patroness gave me a kindly smile, greeted me, "Good morning, Professor Grau," as though the Professor will have his little secrets in private life won't he? and offered me my usual coffee and cream. Police passed outside, and peered through the window. But it was all right, she served me, and went back to filling out her lottery form, for the lottery was one of the first things the counterrevolutionary regime brought back. I have often since pondered this fact: her worldliness.

In the end, I struggled to my secret flat, changed clothes, took a cab to a suburban station, boarded a train, and made my way without incident across the frontier to Vienna. This was the physical end. The spiritual end, as I now think of it, of this great and glorious four-month Revolution, occurred when I met Goldstein, the author of my downfall in Budapest, as a fellow exile in Vienna.

I met him on the Ringstrasse. Goldstein, I remember, greeted me with something like the salutation: "Grau, you cunt!" I replied directly: "What are you angry about, you got me fired." This surprised him. "I had nothing to do with it." I explained about the second friendly chat of Security Minister Masur. "Well," Goldstein said, "you were insecure. Why didn't you answer my idiotic letters? Do you imagine that in the midst of all that upheaval I liked spending time compiling lists of madmen and syphilitics?" I then explained I thought Goldstein was involved in some plot to betray me; I made this explanation because the man seemed genuinely taken aback by my fate.

My explanation seemed reasonable to Goldstein. He calmed down, and invited me to a café on the corner. I remember it was quite hot that day, but he insisted on sitting at a table outside in the full sun, a habit from the old days when we observed security by never speaking in circumstances where it would be easy for others to eaves-drop. It is hard for exiles to learn that in a foreign land few people care about their secrets.

Grau's First Revolution

"Grau," he asked me, "what work did you do during the Revolution?"

I told him about my tours of the countryside, about my plans for the creation of a new people's literature, about ideas for the education of the young.

"So you were never part of things?"

I rather took offense at this. I spoke of the importance of cultural coherence under socialism, of the molding of whole human beings—I can't bear to think of what else. My God, I was young! Goldstein must have seen that I was.

"No, my friend, I did not mean to disparage you. Not at all. I meant . . . for instance, were you ever responsible for the death of someone?"

This put me on guard. I answered only, "Indirectly, perhaps."

"Indirectly, yes. But we all were. Did your department grow during those four months? Did every day you feel the need for more personnel, for greater power, for increased managerial responsibility?"

I said not, I had my hands full as it was.

"Well, you see, that is what I mean about being rather left out of things. And did you have interests outside of your work?"

The question rather surprised me. I replied that of course I did, that in addition to my writing as a philosopher, I was much interested in antique porcelains and ceramics.

"I only ask," Goldstein said, "because most of those at the center of the Revolution had no recreations."

This, it seemed to me, was a matter of the urgency of their work, and I said so.

"That is so, Tibor—may I now call you Tibor?—but they are also a special breed of men. They lack any concept of recreation. This is what principally sets them apart from their imperialistic predecessors, who were also constantly under the impression that they needed more personnel, also driven by the desire for greater power, hopeful for increased managerial scope. And of course only indirectly responsible for the deaths of others. It is the absence of the desire for recreations that marks the true revolutionary. You," he concluded, "are what in my day we would have called an aesthetic young man."

Goldstein could have been no more than five years older than me. Our conversation drifted on to other matters. Goldstein was in the process of setting up a printing business with his uncle in Vienna, and said he looked forward to a vacation on the Lido at Venice. We parted amicably. He seemed to me then an emotional casualty of the Revolution, headed toward an inconsequential life. Now I rather doubt this, and, wherever he is, I wish him well.

I was able to establish myself in Viennese society. I taught at the university, I traveled to England, France, and once even to America. I loved the energy of the Americans and their language, but I could not live there. As with so many my own age, I never lost my revolutionary ideals (although I learned discretion in expounding them). I came to look at the Hungarian Revolution as a glorious failure, a time when I was really and truly alive. And this is why I, like so many others, when the Great Depression swept across the West, dreamed of making a new start, living once again. Again: recovery, renewal, forgetting, giving up, the white page—so many meanings of "again." We drifted into the Soviet Union all through the late twenties and early thirties. Despite my earlier fears—fears which grew weaker in time—I went

Grau's First Revolution

in 1931. I imagined that revolutions were like people, that as they matured they became more understanding, and so more tolerant. I was still so innocent, still so innocent. The worldly lady at the Budapest café would, I'm sure, have known better. So would Goldstein.

Part Three

The Noble Masters

12

From internal evidence, this story seems to have been written in 1940. The document was in a difficult physical condition when I received it. The pages had been carefully torn into even strips, the strips sewn into a muslin bag. The paper Grau used to write on was, however, of exceptionally fine quality, so that the torn edges were crisp. The document was restored by laying each strip between sheets of plastic and then matching up the strips. With one or two exceptions, the restoration has produced a legible manuscript.

Once upon a time there dwelt in the mountains of Transylvania a large colony of troubled dreamers. It was a resort colony, founded by men who had come from Budapest to the mountains, particularly to one dark and still mountain pool. They sought peace, and they hoped for the inspiration which comes from contemplating clouds, pines, snow, and blank blue space. I wish I knew the historical moment when this colony was first established; certainly, it dates back to the eighteenth century, since the most famous basso of the Enlightenment, Hans Glung, gave a performance in the local village of *The Abduction from the Seraglio*, with a seraglio composed of one hundred dark-eyed peasant girls. But in any event, throughout the nineteenth century troubled dreamers of distinction went there. They thought, they talked quietly, they walked, the old ones slowly circling the pond with the aid of malacca canes; sometimes their dulcet singing could be heard echoing in the thin mountain air.

After the upheaval of the First World War, a rather cosmopolitan group of souls in need of peace decided to make this mountain retreat their permanent home. The group included not just Hungarians, although certainly the most substantial elements, from the financial as well as the intellectual point of view, came from this country. There were also elderly Poles, largely retired bank employees; a smattering of smart ladies from Vienna; there was a contingent of Italians, wounded ex-soldiers who had, however, not lost their enthusiasm for the pleasures they could still enjoy. Their voices and songs jarred on the nerves of the Slavs, and aroused ironic comment among the others.

The story I wish to tell is about why this colony failed, why they could not remove themselves from the vices and the sordidness of the world below. It is a sad story, in that they aimed so high. The Budapest masters dreamed of a retreat in which life could be made subordinate to the truths of art, particularly the art of music. Even the Italians good-humoredly spoke of the need for spiritual improvement.

In 1919, the Association des Amateurs d'Art was formally incorporated. The articles of association made certain property the common possession of all members: the concert hall, the promenade that ended in an enclosed pond-café, the hospital. Other property was re-

served by country of origin and special taste, so that the
ladies had a particularly luxurious terrace for themselves,
the Polish bank clerks several hectares of forest in which
they hunted for mushrooms, and the august Hungarians
their beloved lily pond. A generous endowment was provided by a Parisian banker of great age, who said the
Association reminded him of his youth in the Commune.
In short, the struggle for existence had been ended, thanks
to the gifts of nature and vast amounts of cash.

This abundance, the masters hoped, would give those
in the community freedom to develop their souls. The
masters had a plan for how this development would occur
—or perhaps, I should say, they elevated their own
prejudices to the level of a program for all. Historically,
the Hungarian has had an affinity to music. These
Hungarians of the pre-world war generation had a special
love of the music of France. The French music of their
time seemed the summit of spiritual complexity, and
toward an ever-deeper appreciation of this music they
hoped to lead themselves and the lesser orders. I quote
from a manifesto voted by the Association on November
30, 1919:

France, the home of Manet, Monet, and Cézanne—all
recognized as great modern visual masters—is also
the home of great modern masters in music who are
virtually unknown abroad. The masses are lulled by
the flimsiest music; a thousand hands applaud rhyth-
mically after a high note is hit in some opera of no
consequence. But what of the interior vision of
Fauré, the light that suffuses the spiritual struggle of
Chausson, the deep swelling harmonies of Saint-

Saëns, which are beyond pleasure, beyond approval, but which are the inner core of ourselves? We dedicate ourselves to recovering these mysteries.

From this document, it will be evident that ethnic conflict and aesthetic perception were fatally joined in the Association from the very beginning. What Italian, reading this manifesto, could in good conscience maintain his dignity without defending the music of Rossini? And so it happened. Conflict shifted ground from a struggle for food to combat over whose feelings were legitimate.

It was sad this should occur, because the masters had divided the colony's musical activities in a sensible fashion. A professional orchestra imported from Vienna was under the management solely of the Hungarians. Each lower order was allowed to form instrumental or vocal groups which best suited its physiology and interests; for instance, a quartet of Poles formed a dance band called the Sweet-Beats. The Association also sponsored a mixed amateur choir drawn from all groups. Trouble started in the choir.

Choirs are always hotbeds of jealousy, gossip, and intrigue. My father did not want me to sing in the school choir. This choir not only fought among itself but also fought the Association's board of directors. Who should determine the programming? How much of the obligatory salutary French music was required at each concert? After weeks of French orchestral music, the lower orders in the audience were also in a rage, in no mood for compromise. They had once been subjected to a repeat performance of an all-Duparc concert. Special concerts and jam sessions offered insufficient relief. The choir belonged to everyone; its concert was the place to stand up to the masters.

For its first concert, on January 6, 1920, the choir and the board arrived at a geographical and musical compromise: an evening of Swiss hymns. After the first hymn, the Italians, accustomed to projecting their voices over the fields as they sang during the grape harvest, booed. After the second hymn, the Magyar servants joined in. They stamped their feet on the wooden seats of the chairs on which they had been permitted to sit at the back of the hall. The sounds of splintering wood and the booing mingled; elderly gentlemen in flowered waistcoats hopped in the air to make their voices resound over the din; delicate gloved hands of the ladies were pressed ineffectually against their ears to shut out this unseemly commotion. The choir kept going through the mayhem; many of them had griped and conspired with the rebellious in the audience, but when the time for the concert came, they wanted to sing their hymns. I also insisted on singing in the school choir.

Shortly after the choral disaster, the material arrangements of the community were called into question by the case of "Uncle Vardan's Watercolors." It was not a serious matter, but it showed that the masters' desire to edify could not always be realized by edict. The said Vardan was a carpenter with a genuine gift as an amateur painter. Owing to the fact that he preferred to place his canvases on the floor rather than on an easel, and that he was consequently in a contorted position whenever he painted, he soon developed curvature of the spine, and left a relatively small corpus of paintings to bear witness to his talents. The carpenter left these paintings to the Associa-

tion. The masters hung them in the dining hall. His nieces
Caroline and Victoria believed that the light in the dining
hall was bad, and asked the masters to put the paintings
in the foyer of the concert hall, where the light was, they
thought, much better. The masters refused; the light was
in fact worse. At this point, Caroline and Victoria went
to the Surrogate's Court of Transylvania, bypassing the
Association structure entirely, and sued to recover the
paintings as their private property. They won their case.
Because they were pretty and popular girls, no one in the
retreat thought to ostracize them, and everyone knew
how greatly devoted they were to their uncle. Nonetheless,
their court case brought home to everyone a truth they
were in the mountains inclined to forget; namely, that
the power of the masters depended on the belief of others
that they had a right to rule. These young girls, out of
love for Uncle Vardan, simply cut the masters out.

This was in February of 1920. By March, things had
quieted down. Spring came, the call of the new season
seized each section of the community according to its
fashion, and in the joy of work and renewal the masters
were gradually enshrined in people's minds as the guaran-
tors, if not the authors, of so much happiness. And then
came the performance of unpublished, newly discovered
music of Chausson. For these masters, you must realize,
did not simply want to rule: they wanted to lead. The
all-Duparc evening they gradually transformed in memory
to be a great success. The disastrous evening of Swiss
hymns they gradually came to believe was a disaster
because the music was of poor, uncompelling quality.
Surely this great event, the production of an act of an
unknown opera by Chausson, would be a triumph, and

The Noble Masters

surely the community, now if ever, was in a mood to appreciate it.

The decor by a protégé of Bakst, the orchestra conducted by a pupil of Monteux, Madame Quadrapunta in the lead: everything boded well. Musical reporters flooded into the colony from all over Europe, even from Paris itself. There is a wonderful photograph taken in front of the festival hall the day of the premiere, Madame Quadrapunta in costume in the center, five masters on each side of her. The faces of the men are creased in wide smiles, with the eyebrows rather knitted in apprehension. This photograph reminds me of another: my father and his chief clerk standing in front of the bank with Baron de Rothschild, when he made a business trip to Budapest in 1901. Photographs of those posed just before a great event: images of pride and nervousness. In Transylvania, even the lowest echelon of the community —the local servants whom the masters self-consciously treated as, "in the end, part of us"—had caught the spirit of the thing. This led them to commit a fatal blunder.

From the colony's tailor, forty of the locals had ordered full evening dress. They looked marvelous when they entered. Their white, gleaming teeth were echoed in the white of their starched shirt-fronts; the tailor had artfully cut their trousers so that the rather ungainly Transylvanian legs seemed well-proportioned. Each man walked flourishing a silver-topped cane.

The trouble came at the end of the Chausson. To tell the truth, it was not a great work. But, because so much effort had gone into the production, because the community felt its own reputation tied to a good reception of the music, everyone applauded loudly. Now, a man in a polite mood applauds with his hands. An enthusiastic man stamps his feet. This the locals began to do. Unfortunately, the tailor had not planned on them moving athletically, and so made their pants rather tight. As the men gave way to their enthusiasm, their pants began to rip apart. The rips were audible as well as visible. The audience around the locals began to titter and then, as the men became embarrassed, to laugh outright. The local men were surrounded by rich foreigners laughing at them —they who had worked so hard, spent so much money, to do the right thing, to show that they too belonged—and their embarrassment passed quickly to shame, and their shame passed quickly to rage. The chair splitting and mayhem of the Swiss hymn concert began all over again, but now the rioters were not boys out on a spree but men who had been humiliated and who were fighting back. They picked up the chairs, they tore the wood apart with their hands, they broke their silver-topped canes in two. Their faces loomed close to those who a moment before had been laughing and now were screaming. All at once, hurling oaths, they fled in a pack out into the night.

The people at the colony were in truth not like the Parisians, who treated the uproar at the first performance of *Le Sacre du Printemps* as a form of sport. No, they were more serious, more naïve, kinder. When the servants came sullenly into the communal hall for breakfast the next morning, others made an effort to apologize and to soothe them. The masters knew, however, that the structure of their retreat was faulty, and they called a meeting for June 5 to decide what, if anything, they could do. A former chairman of the Budapest Kreditanstalt, Herr von Stein, opened the meeting:

"Ladies and gentlemen, today we face a great crisis

The Noble Masters

in the young life of our fraternity. We have tried to live *with* one another, *for* music. These are noble aims. Yet we are defeated. My friends, I am old. I have seen much in this life, much suffering, many mistakes made with the best intentions. As a banker, I know chance favors the venal; the odds against the worthy are high. Nonetheless, I also know this Association to be no mistake. Given the war we have all so recently lived through, I know that the pursuit of the beautiful is a necessity for the very maintenance of social life, not a youthful illusion.

"Yet we are defeated. The blame may be laid at my door. You are kind to demur"—as several masters shook their heads—"but I must accept the responsibility. For it was I who argued last year that we should have no single leader, no cult figure, and it is I who understand now that so many different people cannot live in harmony, even when every material desire has been satisfied for them, without a single figure in authority.

"The dangers of a single master are obvious. We must find someone with authority who has no desire for power. Such a being is rare. But among all our blessings, this rare creature is also vouchsafed us. I refer to the lady whose husband was one of the leaders of Viennese political life, the Dowager Duchess Irene. This charming, astute, and gracious noblewoman has made her home near our colony for many years; she is universally respected. Let us invite the Dowager Duchess to preside over our most distinguished events, and also over those occasions which may prove sensitive. I believe her presence will chasten those elements of our audience otherwise disposed to mayhem. But, taking a larger view, let me say that her patronage would bring honor to our general endeavor."

The Frog Who Dared to Croak

This speech was received in silence. Many in the boardroom frowned. Herr von Stein meant well, undeniably. But this appeal to the aristocracy seemed to the others wrong. Aristocrats gambled; the leaders of the Association spent their evenings at home reading, when not at a cultural event. Aristocrats maintained lavish salons, at which the finest caviar was heaped in crystal bowls on marble tables. Men like Herr von Stein lent them the money to maintain these ruinous habits. How could a leader worthy of the Association come from the caviar world? What would it mean to have such a leader?

Ten years after it, I still recall the meeting with Our Leader with a nervous stomach. Everyone knows a little of what Our Leader was doing in the thirties—black cars pulling over to the curb on a street in Minsk, the back door opening, and not even men getting out to seize someone, just pointing at him, and like a sheep or a sleepwalker, he would get into the car and you would never see him again. Minsk was the best place an exiled Hungarian Communist could live, since there was a local Institute of Magyar Language Studies. Yet, once he arrived there, the exile was ambushed; a terrible joke, except no one was laughing. In fact, the memory of Our Leader's Minsk that stays most strongly in my mind is of the silence of the place; silence, snow, and dust in the corridors of the police stations.

I had a friend, Zamotin, who knew Our Leader as a boy in Tashkent. After Our Leader became Our Leader, that is, the chief Party hack in Minsk, that is, an Oriental potentate on his share of glorious Communist turf, he would occasionally be overcome with a maudlin desire to see his old boyhood friend, to talk with someone in the

The Noble Masters

Tashkent dialect, to reminisce. These moods would come upon Our Leader suddenly, at any time of the day or night, and he would send a car to find Zamotin and bring him to Leader Headquarters. Poor Zamotin would be in a restaurant or in bed sleeping and this car full of men who were obviously guards would appear, and he didn't know if he was going to jail or just to another boozy evening with his childhood friend. He never knew, because Our Leader had such a temper, if he might say something that would lead Our Leader instantly to order his death. Of course, Our Leader didn't telephone in advance. The result of Zamotin's "friendship" with Our Leader was not what you would think. People did not try to curry favor with Zamotin, as they might have in a society where someone had the ear of a king. No, they stayed away from him as though he had a fatal disease.

Now, I also feared Zamotin—not that he was in any way an ambitious or evil man who might whisper in Our Leader's ear: "Take this one away next"; Zamotin was a meek accountant with an interest in T'ang porcelain—I, too, feared that I might be with Zamotin one day when the car filled with guards would arrive and perhaps would take me to a death camp. But I have always had an interest in pottery, and Zamotin was one of the few people in Minsk I could talk to about it. It certainly was, or at least seemed, a safe subject, and so we would even discuss it in cafés or restaurants, without too much fear of the spies. You have to remember, people did not talk much, maybe about the weather, or simply the recitation of the latest production figures, or other trivia, in public, because the spies were everywhere. So to see two men talking with passion at all in a restaurant was something of an oddity in those days.

The Frog Who Dared to Croak

Well, one evening it happened. And on the worst evening; I had drunk too much vodka because it was so cold in the room I lived in then. Zamotin and I were in a café discussing a problem of lacquer technique in Hunan when the car appeared. The driver said to Zamotin that he was to come and bring whomever else he was with; this man, of course, did not tell us where, so I thought, Well, Grau, somehow your books will survive, and maybe even these scraps of autobiography, so that people will know you were not just another casualty. But when we got into the car, the guard next to the driver told us: "Our Leader is in a merry mood tonight and he wants to have a party; so we are to find people for him to have a party with." I wondered a bit at this, and then realized how smart Our Leader must be. If he got drunk at his party with the innumerable political hacks who normally surrounded him, he might indiscreetly let loose some secret, which one of the hacks might use to his own advantage, or grant some favor. So a more relaxed party for Our Leader would be the roundup of a nobody like Zamotin off the streets, and anyone else Zamotin was with, because such persons were likely to be as inoffensive as he.

Now, I want to remember just exactly how we went into Leader Headquarters. It had formerly been the palace of a prince. In the car there were the two guards in front, and in the back—this was an immense limousine—two guards facing us, they on the jump seats, we on the banquette. As I remember, the banquette was red plush, and the back was curtained all around. The jump-seat guards remained immobile, their hands folded in their laps until we must have come to a designated spot close to Leader Headquarters; at that point they both took out large guns from shoulder holsters, and held the guns in their laps. Then, when we must have come to the outer walls of the building itself, the guard next to the driver got out. I could hear various gates closing and unclosing as we drove in very slowly. The car stopped and we were in a sort of concrete square box. Six new guards surrounded the car, we two merrymakers were ordered to get out, and while four of the guards aimed their guns at us, the other two searched us very thoroughly—and I must say, very courteously. Then, and here was the interesting thing, the new guards took the guns away from the guards in the car and searched *them*.

I seem to recall reading that the palace guards of Louis XIV worked in the following way: a small flourish of trumpets was given as the visitor entered the outer gates of Versailles. As one got to the actual building, a longer and louder flourish of trumpets was given, with a larger band of trumpeters. By the time you actually entered the royal presence, a deafening peal of horn music announced your arrival, and probably the fact you were now suffering from a migraine added to your nervousness at being received by the king, reduced you to a state in which it was difficult to say anything, and of course the king would interpret this as properly deferential modesty.

In the Leader Headquarters, once the searching was over in the rectangular concrete room, we simply walked through a steel-door entry into a bare room with four chairs and a desk, the six new guards lined up against one wall with another steel door in it. We were motioned to sit down. We did. Suddenly the door opened, and there was Our Leader smiling and holding the door open for us and waving us in with his other hand and saying cordially to Zamotin, "Hello, my dear, who is this you have brought for me?"

"I do not believe there is any finer pottery in the world than in Tashkent."

"Nor do I, Leader."

"Please, have more vodka, or would you prefer good Russian champagne?"

"Well . . . what will you have, Zamotin? I can't decide."

While Our Leader poured Zamotin what must have been his tenth vodka (and the poor man hadn't had any food all day, since the ration cards were for twenty days of food for each month), I racked my brains to think of some other safe subject.

"Tell me, Comrade Grau, what is it technically that makes the pottery of Tashkent so superior to all other pots?"

What is one to say about some rough peasant stewpot compared to a piece of T'ang porcelain?

"Principally the quality of the Tashkent soil, Leader."

"You mean the workmanship is not also superior?"

"That, too."

"But, come, which is it, the soil or the hand that turns it on the wheel?" Our Leader was beginning to get annoyed; I also had the feeling that he wanted me to say something which would fit into a plan of his, but I couldn't see what.

"May I now have some champagne, Leader?"

"Of course, if it will loosen your tongue. You prefer the coupe or the tulip shape for champagne?"

"The tulip, Comrade Leader."

"So, you still retain bourgeois taste, I see. Well, my

friend, what about my question—is it the soil or the hand that turns the wheel?"

Herr von Stein asked, after a moment of silence, whether the others would accede to his proposal. A portly Transylvanian, really one of the few distinguished men among that horde, and their representative to the Association, rose to reply.

"I suppose I must preface my answer to our distinguished colleague with an apology. It is an apology for my people, who are known to be boisterous and crude. I accept this, as one must accept all that is inescapable; although I would point out that many of the servants here came recently from other places. In any event, Herr von Stein, could we not pursue our noble experiment in pure form one time more? Perhaps more elevating music than Swiss hymns, but less demanding music than an opera of Chausson, might create true interest, and this interest might lead to self-discipline. The discipline you propose is external; you propose to use personal authority to seduce the rabble into respect for the beautiful and the good. Is not the beautiful defiled when it is presumed too feeble to justify itself?"

"I do not permit silence, Comrade Grau."

"You must forgive me, Comrade Our Leader, but your question is a difficult one. I want to give you a true answer."

"Zamotin, does this man know anything about the art of pottery?"

Thank God, Zamotin had his wits about him. He replied instantly: "To tell the truth, my dear friend, he is an idiot on this subject. But I pity him, and I implore you to pity him, since he only sought to engage you in discussion on pottery to give you pleasure. His ignorance is exposed, but the foolish words come only from a desire to please. You and I may confidently say to Comrade Tibor that we know it is both the soil and the hand that turns the wheel. We know in Tashkent work and nature to be one. This is the answer our poor friend should have given, and now he knows what to say when next the subject comes up."

"Repeat it, Grau."

"Of course, Comrade Leader. The reason Tashkent pottery—"

"No, repeat everything Zamotin said."

"I . . . I spoke out of ignorance."

"Don't disobey me! Repeat all of it in your own words."

"I am, well, then, I am an idiot on this subject. I ask you—"

"No, my friend, you beg me."

"Yes, I beg you to pity me, since I only sought to discuss these matters in order to give you pleasure. But now I know, thanks to your instruction—"

"Well, let us not leave our dear comrade Zamotin out, my friend."

"Yes, thanks to Comrade Zamotin and your instruction, I know that it is both the hand and the soil, I mean, the soil and the hand that turns the wheel, that create the special excellence of Tashkent pottery. This is because, in Tashkent, work and nature are as one."

"Good. Now I will give you more champagne—but in a coupe."

Herr von Stein considered the local representative's words carefully. He did not feel personally offended.

"I am moved," he said, "by all that our distinguished colleague has said. And I quite agree, the beautiful is

The Noble Masters

defiled when we lose faith in its power to compel, in and of itself. But I recall to you all another of our distinguished colleague's ideas, which seems to me equally true. In speaking of his unfortunate compatriots he remarked that one must accept what is inescapable . . ."

What is inescapable? I have two or three times, when I thought we would all soon go to dust, told people about the conversation with Our Leader. My listeners asked me, "But didn't you feel humiliated?," and I replied that in truth I did not. I could not escape. To die through giving the wrong answer about those wretched Tashkent pots would be no more or less noble than to die through telling our dear comrade Our Leader what I thought of him.

The word "noble" applies in society only to those who keep silent for the sake of the liberty of others: prisoners under interrogation. When I am silent in an Academy of Literature meeting to save my own skin, I am not noble. The noble ideals of the Association: men in a great mass around the mountain pond singing the "Anvil Chorus." Sometimes I feel that my nobility lies simply in my endurance. The noble Margrave von Grau, ironic about my early enthusiasms, never ironic about my brown bear. The Margrave von Grau had endurance—his capacity for endless meetings at the bank, for working long hours— and yet this fortitude could not really be described as "noble." Of course the societies of the past are different from what we have established in this successful Revolution, which itself has endured the attacks of the capitalist stooges, the counterrevolutionaries in 1919, and the terrible attacks of the enemies who, however, last year became our friends, the German / Italian / Japanese. At a Minsk Academy of Literature meeting it was my privilege to speak on the theme "The Nobility of Survival," but it was exactly this theme that the portly local representative has called into question. We may say that Herr von Stein represents the willingness of the past to compromise with the present for the sake of the survival of culture, and that his distinguished adversary represents the nobility of beauty willing to perish, but then, this dignified man comes from a backward country.

"It is inescapably a fact that the first six months of our Association have produced great suffering for foreigner and local alike. If there is no pleasure in our community, what is the reason to continue it? We might as well return to the world below. I make my proposal as an effective, if not the purest, means of guaranteeing that we can enjoy the pleasures of art in serenity."

The board meeting closed without a decision about Herr von Stein's proposal. As is the way with meetings in which everyone vows to be discreet, the whole community soon knew every detail of the proceedings. For the Italians, the argument between Herr von Stein and the Transylvanian provided material for endless discussion, requiring endless cups of coffee. The locals spoke darkly of a plot, and threatened to form a union. The Viennese ladies found it all unseemly and absorbing. Rehearsals soon became less a matter of practicing music than of perfecting arguments. Men winked knowingly at Herr von Stein as he took his daily walk around the lily pond.

Herr von Stein became increasingly depressed. He had known how difficult a retreat would be practically, but he had underestimated the sheer pleasure his flock would take in the difficulties of making the experiment work. Other masters retreated into themselves; suddenly there

The Noble Masters

was a vogue for Marcel Proust. Oddly, several of the masters themselves began to take up writing, either reworking student theses they had abandoned when young, or beginning short stories, memoirs, or political tracts whose content they had vaguely thought about from time to time, but had never felt impelled to set down on paper.

The very freedom from material care of the colony encouraged gossip among the lower orders, individual artistic enterprise among the elite. At first in private, and then in public, people of all sorts began saying the unspeakable: they were bored with music. It became chic to be bored with music; instead of attending concerts, one took a walk with friends, or remained in one's room creating. Herr von Stein, roused from his own depression, finally took matters in hand by calling another meeting of the masters.

"My friends, in the last two weeks we have learned a hard lesson. The aspirations inscribed in our charter have ceased to move the members of our community. Concert attendance is appalling. People demand of me that the bar stay open until the early hours of the morning. The counterpoint of gossip has become our music. Yes, a hard lesson. I conclude that only we masters, with a very few others like our esteemed Transylvanian colleague, only we can live according to the ideals of the Association. The others must be sent into exile from this exile."

The shock was less than one might have supposed—exile. Leaving a country where one wasn't wanted for a country where one didn't matter. Private events occupy one more. The death of one's father, overwhelming because there is no one to share it with who knew him.

The Frog Who Dared to Croak

Small events in private life also occupy one more: one's ration cards, the exact wording on one's work permit. These measure precisely how much one is allowed to belong.

The shock was less than one might have supposed. In establishing the Association, the masters had acted from generous, noble, and civilized motives. But they had only their generosity, nobility, and civility to sustain them. When these virtues meet no appreciation, they naturally grow weaker. Moreover, these masters were tired, tired from years of anxiety in the guarding of their families and their fortunes during the war, tired from all the effort of beginning over again in the mountains. And so this second proposal of Herr von Stein's was entertained more favorably. It was decided that the board of directors would give itself two weeks to reflect. In the meantime, the board decided to reduce the concert schedule, to import a second tailor, and to delegate the task of weekly menu composition to Caroline and Victoria. A month later, the board met again. The decision was taken: all except the masters and a few chosen others would be asked to leave. Herr von Stein's speech, at the final general assembly meeting, was the essence of tact:

"The request I put before you today is one your masters make reluctantly. You must consider it less a reflection upon yourselves than upon us. We invited all of you here to the mountains, hoping that a community dedicated to the highest ideals of the musical art might flourish away from the vulgarities of the city. We made this community possible for you in every way. It was our gift. We made you a gift of art.

"Now, you all must recall Christmastimes from your childhood when a maiden aunt, or distant cousin, sent

The Noble Masters

you a gift you had no need or desire for: a penknife, useless for a strong boy, or a tea cozy, or a pair of woolen socks that were too short. The maiden aunt could not be blamed for sending you these gifts, and you must not blame us if our gift, too, has proved unsuitable.

"There is no need to recount the troubles of our Association, nor, to tell the truth, have I the heart to do so. You must think of the months you have spent here as an interlude in lives that are to be devoted to other interests. I hope that sometime in the future you will look back to these months, to the meals we have shared together, to the walks we have taken, as something precious. Above all, I hope strains of music will float back into your memory. Today, I know it well, you are relieved that there is no music, only silence or chatter, but one day, when you are walking, or in the bath, or resting before dinner, a melody will come into your mind, a fragile soft melody that will bring these months back to you in a new way and will give you courage in facing the hardships of life. All I have wanted for you is the inner strength of knowing beauty. This is the gift your masters made to you, and there will come a time, I assure you, a time of sorrow or of self-doubt, when in memory you will accept our gift with gratitude."

The locals were barely listening. They could not wait to go down to town to visit a new tailor, someone who specialized in double-vented suits with tassels. The girls cried, but they, too, had accepted the masters' decision that they must leave. Victoria, drying her tears and clutching the one painting of Uncle's she had decided to take (leaving the rest as a present to the colony), looked at Caroline, and said, "I want to meet a big, black-eyed blond." Caroline was shocked for a moment, and then giggled conspiratorially. The elderly ladies sighed, gathered up their voluminous shawls and capacious handbags, and remarked that one might still see a bit of the "season" in Vienna.

Two days after Herr von Stein's speech, the masters were alone. That evening they commanded the orchestra to play the Chausson *Poème*, with the orchestra's leader as soloist. It is a melancholy piece, but the melancholy stops short of despair. Major and minor harmonies succeed each other as do light and shade when fast-moving clouds reign in the sky. In the concert hall built for two thousand, a small band of one hundred sat silent and rapt in the center.

The moan of Chausson's *Poème* was ceaseless—a siren calling us to perpetual regret. And as we sat huddled there, a small band in the dark, abandoned auditorium, I reflected that our fate was just: no one can give to another more than permission to exist, and that permission entails all manner of mistakes, stupidities, and waywardness. Our Leader did not give such permission and he was evil. My masters gave it and were good. In solitude, drawn out of ourselves to this austere melody, finally we were free.

Part Four

A War Diary

13

*This document is part of a diary Grau kept during the
Second World War. The document is a small notebook
bound with a metal spiral; fragments of pages torn out
still adhere to the spine. There are no other physical traces
of alteration or concealment.*

*For the benefit of younger readers or those unfamiliar
with wartime regulations, a curious feature of this diary
should be noted: it is written in German, like all Grau's
"private" writing. A soldier cannot in good conscience observe security by writing in the language of his enemy.*

*After months of bitter struggle in the spring of 1944,
the Russian army led by General Rokossovsky swept suddenly into the city of Minsk. The victory was a decisive
step in pushing the Germans out of Belorussia. By taking
Minsk so swiftly, the Russian army also took large numbers of German troops. The work of interrogating these
prisoners occupied a cadre of German-speaking soldiers
for several months in Minsk. Grau tells us in the diary
that he was able to avoid this work, and follow the forward movement of the Russian army as it swept toward
the Hungarian and Polish borders. Grau says he did this
because he hated Minsk and hoped to reenter Hungary;
he does not say how great were the dangers to which he*

exposed himself in working as a translator on the front lines, for the Russians not only met bitter German resistance but traveled through a countryside ravaged by cholera. The reader also ought to know that the mass of prisoners left behind in Minsk were subject to the most brutal treatment at the hands of their Russian captors.

The diary opens with entries made in the spring of 1944, when the Russian army headed for Minsk was disorganized and short of supplies. Traps like the one Grau fell into were common.

(Undated): My face must be some sort of scale for the soldiers. When we have a good day, just marching, no crazed fire from retreating Germans, rations for everyone, they call me grandpapa. On a bad day, I am papa. Today I was grandpapa.

(Undated): Another grandpapa day.

(Undated): Nine days of marching come to an end. At 14:00 this afternoon, we joined a convoy headed for Minsk. Home?

June 19: The convoy moves to the south slowly. The remnants of a German brigade are somewhere ahead of us in disorderly retreat. Pains in my shoulder are becoming worse.

(Undated): I had a long talk with the captain this morning. I can't make things clearer. I am perfectly willing to continue as interpreter for captured officers, no objection whatever; I simply want to move with the lines, not stay "home" in Minsk. He seemed to understand my point about efficient and immediate interrogations, but made

A War Diary

all the usual objections about my age and physical condition. The outcome is indeterminate.

(Undated): The idiot! He's moved us to a place where we are caught among streams of the retreating German brigade. The remains of our squad, in one truck, are temporarily cut off from the convoy body. Germans all around us, about three kilometers away. The village itself is rather pretty; icons the peasants had hidden away were brought into the church during the war, and they look like blue and gold jewels against the white walls. If we don't draw attention to ourselves, we may be safe. The roads through the village are not as good as those going around it, and the Germans may simply bypass us.

Dear Natalie,

I am writing you as though this letter could reach you. I am in a village; we are surrounded by retreating German forces. Everyone in the village moves silently. Our hope is simply that they will pass by this seemingly deserted place. It seems a good moment, therefore, to speak to you, not so much to confess, or even to explain, as to settle accounts.

Tolstoy's famous remark is that each unhappy family is unhappy in its special way. Once, my dear one, I believed this was true of us. Our quarrels, your tears, my resentful silences, all seemed so important because they were produced by the intersection of our ever so complex personalities, seeking fulfillment in a world where no one really understood us, and so forth and so on. The war has forced me to change my views. Suffering in war is a great common denominator. But what is common is not therefore trivial, nor even uniform. I believe we, my darling, have been unhappy in rather interesting ways. In dissecting this interesting unhappiness, I wish merely to caution you against thinking that I now believe our sorrows were therefore more important than the sorrows of people who had little money or ill health. Tolstoy, we may say, was correct to remark on the fertile variety of human suffering, but this variety has an academic, rather than a moral, value.

Let us begin with your feelings of inadequacy. They, after all, began our emotional career together. Do you remember those early days when you came to my lectures in Minsk? How you wrote down every word, how after class you would ask me anxiously if you had understood such and such a point about Hegel, or about the dialectical evolution of the argument in *Capital* itself? Do you remember when we first met for cups of tea in the university dining hall the comment we aroused, or the day when I remarked that I was a confirmed bachelor whose students were his children, and you said that my genius should be passed on in a more direct way? Never, Natalie, could I ever suspect you of flattery, you were much too ingenuous. No, I felt truly flattered by your adoration. I, too, believed I was a genius—we had a felicitous meeting of minds on this point—and your praise was water on parched earth. Only later did I learn that self-abasement, the idolatrous worship of a young woman for an older man, can also have its element of smug self-satisfaction. I should have noticed this when, after we had begun our relations, you began scornfully to speak of the opinions of other students as "childish." But I didn't notice.

A War Diary

Now, you will recall that almost from our wedding day you began to worry about whether you were boring me. At first, remember, it was a question: "Tibor, am I boring you?" Again so flattering, it permitted me to display a handsome generosity and say, "Of course not, your observation about X contains a fascinating idea, namely . . ." Then it became a statement, an accusation. "Tibor, I am boring you." This was progress in a way, since it showed you thought I didn't have a right to be bored, and entirely correct you were. Had matters stopped there, I believe our marriage would have eventually been straightened out. Either I would have left the castle of my egotism and become interested in you, or you would have eventually left me, in anger and in pride. But matters did not stop there. You tried to become "interesting."

Let us face directly your pot-making. Your two years of apprenticeship, all those interesting "student" pots, your endless reports to me about the evolution of your artistic development—confess that all these efforts were in large part directed toward showing me that we had something in common, a practitioner paired with a connoisseur of pottery. Confess that, and I will confess that my indifference was appalling, appalling because I truly had no feelings one way or another about your efforts, and reacted only to the fact that you were pleading for recognition. This made me feel a certain contempt for you. And why, I ask you, why should I have felt this contempt? Is it not entirely honorable for one human being to seek recognition from another? The light is gone. I must stop.

(Undated): When the Germans detected us yesterday, they had no thought of blowing up the village. They needed men to push a truck out of a ditch. They needed, more immediately, food, water, and a place to let their wounded rest for a few hours. We had in the village enough ammunition to put up a token resistance, but we had these more precious requisites of temporary peace as well.

Early this morning, I woke to find five peasants in my room. They had taken my gun. They pointed it at me, and told me to go outside, where I joined two other men, one from my squad, one a refugee in the village. We were marched to the last house in the town. A German sergeant was outside it. The peasants held up a strip of yellow cloth in front of our faces. We understood, the sergeant understood. We three were Jews; the peasants were offering us, as they might have dangled a chicken at market, in order to make a deal with the German. Take the Jews and go. The peasants were behind the times; Germans were no longer taking Jews as forced laborers. Now they were under orders to kill any and all Jews they encountered. I knew the new rule.

I began to talk to the German sergeant. He could speak no Russian, the peasants could speak no German. Jew I might be, but he could converse with me. "You are a Jewish officer; I am obliged to shoot you." I replied that I understood this full well, and that I would explain to the others. I said to the peasants, "He wants food. He will take food and take only me prisoner." From their pockets, the peasants took out some moldy potatoes and onions. I said to the German, "They want you to take the food only if you will shoot the other Jews as well"—it was just something about his face that prompted me to do this wild thing. I was right; his mouth puckered in disgust.

A War Diary

The peasants misunderstood. They pushed the Jewish refugee forward, saying, "Here, here is another Jew. Take him as well as the potatoes." The refugee wailed; it was not fair, the cloth was his, the peasants took the cloth from him. I said to the German, "They say this one has meat on him, you can work him or whatever, he has meat." The German turned away. He said nothing. The refugee began weeping and wailing, until one of the peasants hit him in the back with my rifle butt. The refugee collapsed on the ground; the blow must have done something to his spine.

The German asked me why I spoke such good German. I answered truthfully: that I was a Hungarian, that I had learned German as a child better than I had learned to read and write my own language. "You speak well," he said. "You and the Jew soldier, help us push the truck out of the ditch." He took the potatoes from the peasants. They watched us dislodge the truck. And then the miracle; he got into the truck, he drove away. He left us at the edge of the village, the peasants jabbering, the refugee motionless on the ground, the soldier and myself sweating.

I was sure that the peasants would kill me and the other soldier they had rounded up for market. However, their fear for themselves was the only thing on their minds; we were simply driven out into the forest. I found the truck we had hidden in the woods. The soldier and I finally started the truck and were able to drive to Slovon, a larger village, without encountering any Germans. Today, a message came to this village from the other, asking for help; a new group of Germans is bearing down on them, and the villagers have exhausted both their ammunition and their food. I was able to intercept the message, and to destroy it. So many would have approved of this death-dealing interception: Bruno, Masur, and— for a different reason, but does that matter?—Goldstein.

(Undated): I continue to think about Slovon. Say the Fascists overrun such a village. One of the men puts up a feeble resistance, fires a shot that hits a German boy in the leg. In retaliation, the Fascists lock up all the men in the village in the church, set fire to it, and shoot those who try to escape the burning building. This is barbarism. When, however, we retake that village, we capture fifty German boys. The night of their capture, shots are heard; the next morning, fifty dead bodies appear in a heap in the village square. They were shot trying to escape, of course. This is simply the way of war. In the months of the German retreat, I have thought over and over about this photography of death, this printing of a positive from a negative. I have thought about it, Natalie, because it makes me ask why the death of one man, peacefully in his bed, my father, surrounded by nurses in a Zurich hospital, why this death has been for me so much more terrible than the photography of death in war.

You will say, it is only natural so. One feels the death of a father in a personal way one can never feel the death of strangers. But here, my darling, is the curious thing. My father was never so alive to me as after he died. I felt him constantly with me, saying, "Yes, Tibor, it is good you teach," when I went back to my post in Vienna after his funeral; saying, "A young man should travel, it is good," when I went on my journey later to England and America; looking at me with that ironic smile of his and saying softly, "So you are going away from us," when

A War Diary

I decided to move to Russia, with that undertone of bit-terness that only I could hear, only I could understand.

So much more alive than when he was alive. I felt there was everything left unsaid between us, that as a child and as a young man I had really never gotten to know him. And this depressed me, I now see for how long and how much. Nothing seemed as real as this man I could not recover, no love as great as this love I had missed in the flesh. My depression made me feel cold—but I was not cold. I was haunted by loss.

You see, my dear one, the ledger of love is not like an accountant's book of losses and gains. There are certain love-losses which can never be recouped. Had I, as a young professor, a thousand workers as lovers, it would never have made up for my love as a boy of men in the Munici-pal Park. Longing cannot be erased once it is registered in the heart. Later, the loss of a man I had known but not known—my father—kept me from new love. For instance, in Minsk in 1933 I met a boy who I imagined would make the perfect love for me. He was younger, eighteen. Throughout my life, before, I had sought out older men, even during my twenties, always someone older and more powerful. As is the way of photography in love as well as death, I thought the positive of these negatives, the posi-tive being young and vulnerable, would bring me that con-summate love I missed with the others. Piotr was tall, but undernourished, as were most children of the Revolution. He had blond hair and a wispy goatee, worn like Lenin's, although it did not suit his hatchet-shaped face. He worked in a printer's shop and hoped to become a designer of revolutionary posters. Different from you, he was com-pletely unself-conscious, unconcerned about being or not being an artist—forgive me. Well, this boy fell in love with me first, another change. He came to my apartment near the station, and we would sit and talk about life. He was innocent in the sense that he was blank; he loved his father and mother, who were workers, just as a young man should; he obeyed traffic wardens, helped old ladies onto buses. He never sought my approval for his life, only my affection. He loved me in the same open way he dealt with the rest of the world. Now, shall I tell you what happened? I soon felt indifferent to him. I even felt indifferent to the smooth, soft skin of his body, which had originally excited me, his smooth, V-shaped back, his straight thighs. He left me dignified notes saying he would not impose upon me, but that if I wanted him, even just as a friend, he was always ready to come see me; he behaved well. After a few months, I never called.

When I say I was haunted, I don't mean that my father would speak directly to me whenever I gazed at Piotr. He was, if I may put it so, a more ingenious ghost. Nothing I could have would even measure up to what I could no longer have. As a child, I knew my father, for all his chagrin at my overly sensitive ways, I knew my father would always be there when I wanted him. "Yes, here, Tibor, I have been waiting for you, let us go together, let us go for a walk, let us go to the bank and you can play with the vault doors; the guards, everyone there, love you. Let us go." I might consent, as though conferring a favor. But now this event of his death meant we could not go together, and so I was eager. The outside world seemed hollow; no love in it could ever equal this gentle absence.

I tell you all this, Natalie, as a tribute. You appeared to offer the hope that this depression, my haunting, might

A War Diary

be put to an end. I would start a family of my own, become a father myself. Nothing would have pleased him more.

July 9, 1944: I am staring at the house that used to be the home of the Minsk Academy of Literature. All that is left of the house is the back wall of the ground floor. The Germans made a beautiful hit on the building. I should be thinking: What a tragedy, the home in which writers from this province met weekly no longer exists, the library on the second floor—although it did not contain many books—has disappeared, there is rubble instead of culture. Instead, I am thinking: Wonderful, the little room at the back of the third floor, where the censor for the town of Minsk worked, is destroyed. The censor will no longer practice word surgery next to a cubbyhole in which he made tea; he decided to give you a cup or not, depending on what he thought of your most recent production. Perhaps the censor will become discouraged if he has to work in a bare office like other functionaries. Perhaps he will give up. I am also thinking about the meeting room, the scene of so many lies, of people paying tribute to the linguistic theory of Joseph Stalin while their thoughts were on who in the writers' chamber was an informer. This room of lies, of homage to the power of death made in the name of literature, is gone, bombed, destroyed. I spent month after month imagining how to blow it up, and here the Germans did it for me.

So you see, when I think of "our" triumph over the Fascist enemy, I have a problem.

I turn around and stare at the building that houses the philosophy, ancient history, and art departments of the University of Minsk. The Germans rather botched things here. An incendiary shell has gutted the ground floor, but this floor contained mostly marble statues of classical authors, and the statues did not shatter during the fire, just turned black. So, in place of the bust of Cicero in red and white marble, one now sees what appears to be a bust of Cicero in porphyry, an entirely more valuable material. I enter the building. There is smoke damage in the stairwell, and even many months after the attack, one still gets a whiff of the smoke itself. I enter my office on the second floor. The Oriental rug Aunt Doreen gave me has been stolen, but no one has taken the two Sèvres vases from my father. Strange, since the rug was rather garish and the vases are exquisite. Also, my books have been looted in the most peculiar way. The complete set of Marx is of course intact; no one in his right mind would think of . . . but someone has taken the *Authorized Selections from Saint-Simon,* while leaving behind *The Complete Works of Fourier,* and these works, both stylistically and ideologically, belong together. Of course, the authorized Saint-Simon was bound in paper made to look like leather, while the Fourier was more nakedly paperbound. The copy of Proust's *Jean Santeuil* is gone, but the *A la Recherche* is here. Perhaps there were two different looters, a gross looter who wanted a brightly colored rug and a leather-bound book, and a more refined, scholarly thief who already possessed Proust's masterwork but wanted to add its precursor to his own library.

My chair still seems in good order. I have a special chair, you know, given me by my Minsk colleagues upon the publication of *Realism and Reality.* It tilts backward and swivels to the side.

Now I make the inventory of my desk. Top left drawer:

black inkwell, stolen. Pens and nibs, all present and accounted for. Paper clips, mostly present. The middle left drawer contained the manuscript of *Reason and Power.* Someone has been correcting it! This is incredible. Some thief sat in this room, in my swivel chair, and actually had the gall to start correcting my manuscript. Could the censor have moved his office over here and perhaps, in idle moments, doodling censorially as it were, cast his pen across my text? No, nothing has been smartened up ideologically. The correction on page 56, for instance, changes the sentence, "Rationality does not realize itself but is realized by the matrix of power," to the sentence, "Reason does not speak of its own accord; it must be made to speak, prompted by exhaustion, disappointment, or simply the spirit of mischief." Much better, isn't it? I think I'll keep that one. Bottom drawer: the pictures of my father, my aunt, and my Viennese friend. Someone has shattered the glass of all three photos, and drawn a mustache on my aunt. I understand destroying something with one's mind, like my manuscript, but this . . .

(Undated): Absence. Absence from "home." Absence in Russia before the war became my measure of desire. Do you remember the man I told you about, the one I had a crush on who turned out to be a police spy? You were comforting about him, too—such a betrayal, poor sweet one, it is all over. In the years after my father's death, I thought about this policeman constantly, especially when I was able to read his report on me, which my father managed to confiscate. A man desires the Other, the Impossible. His uniform, I kept wishing I had seen him in his uniform, blue tunic with dull metal buttons, I kept wishing we could have made love with his tunic on, and his trousers dropped down around his ankles, his stalk and flower waving under his tunic, yes, I would dream of this until I came. An impossibility made out of the other impossibility, that I should fall in love with a man doing his job.

I once met Piotr on the street and began screaming at him, words with no meaning; he simply waited until the fit was over, and then took me to an inn for tea. Don't tell me—everyone feels this way after a parent's death. You see how wrong Tolstoy was; everyone feels unhappiness because it is life. All I can claim as special was the coincidence in some diabolical horoscope between my signs of grief and the grief which possessed your country. This astral coincidence meant simply that no one took much notice of my case; there were so many depressed people in Russia before the war.

(Undated): The rubble is cleared from the courtyard and I at last return to my apartment. The building is in one of the few streets of Minsk to show no traces of war. The dustcovers over the furniture are exactly as my housekeeper placed them when we were forced to leave. There is a smell of smoke in my apartment—how this would have worried me in the old days! Despite all my housekeeper's efforts to clean away the presence of Natalie— and she so resented the intrusion of the young wife into the professor's home—there are little things that remind me of Natalie. The water jug she made. The hairbrush she gave me.

I have just tried to find you. They say at your flat that you moved a year before the Germans came. I said to the concierge, "She was my wife."

She looked sad. "So many have died."

"No, no, we were divorced." I don't know why I said this to her, but I thought I had to justify my questions.

"Divorced? You want her back?" She glowed at me conspiratorially.

"No, I am just trying to find her."

"Of course she will have you back. When you find her, here is my advice: do not apologize, do not explain. Tell her you are hungry, you want to eat—you understand me?"

"But you don't know where my wife moved?"

"No, comrade, I came here after she had gone. But still, my advice is good."

I left you in our love-accounts with the admission of a great debt I owe you: you broke the spell of my father's death. I will not dwell here upon my oft-expressed feeling of gratitude for your understanding in the bedroom, except to say I realize now how angry your tolerance made me. You said you didn't mind, but it would have been better if you had been more demanding of me, not content to finish your pleasure by yourself, me halfway to sleep at your side. Much better. You should have said, "Tibor, I want a man who can satisfy me." Perhaps this would have led to a clean break, or—who knows?—perhaps faced with the challenge, I might have succeeded in doing so. One wants to be all things to all people. As it was, we discussed the baby that was surely on its way. So kind, so comforting, so humiliating.

Well, I want to extract one confession from you: admit to me you were relieved when this blessed event failed to materialize. But you kept the upper hand by never making that admission. No, again you were understanding and sweet, so that the burden of this failure, for whatever physiological or astrological reasons, was on

The Frog Who Dared to Croak

my shoulders. It is this sweet understanding on your part that was, I believe, the great reason our marriage failed.

I want to impress on you one fact, surprising as it may seem in view of what I just wrote: I loved you. I loved you simply for existing. The adventure failed—but that's usually the way of adventures. There was no need for you to try to earn this love; you cannot earn love. I can tell you exactly what I loved about our life: entertaining, discussing books, the ritual of tea in the afternoon, the simplest things. And all these set with the increasing barrenness of our bedroom life, a barren ending that set me free of Father. See, I have carried on, Father, I have children— Our failure to produce these creatures gradually extinguished my aching desire that I might speak to him, that I could speak to him. A great, if unintended, gift. Natalie, you may find it strange that I put a profession of love in so egotistical a form. But how else can I acknowledge a real debt?

(Undated): I have carried the day with my *capitaine*. When the brigade moves out, I will do front-line interrogation. I have not succeeded in acquiring an aide who can read and write: the note-taking will go on as before. Six of my old group of guards are assigned to me, but which six, *le capitaine* does not yet know, because the muster roll is a shambles. He has asked me to help the adjutant put the muster roll in order.

(Undated): The muster roll remains incomplete; I have been working on it, and at least some progress has been made. Two platoons have, clearly, deserted from B group, and one from H group. If we are responsible for administering these cases by reconscripting them, we will be

A War Diary

in Minsk forever. The number of personnel involved is trivial, of course.

(Undated): We made up some beautiful names today to fill B group: Arkady A. Gerolstein was my favorite.

(Undated): The muster is complete. *Le capitaine* sent the supplementary forms to central bureau as well. The news is full of the usual claims; however, it does seem, reading between the lines, that the Germans are in full-scale retreat.

(Undated): It is a month since I have written in this journal. From the routing orders we received when we left Minsk two weeks ago, it appears we are heading southwest to the Hungarian border. After Stry, it was very difficult to tell precisely where on the border we are destined, if in fact we go there. Today we have suddenly been ordered to halt.

I have a demon. He said: go to your room, go upstairs, Tibor, go to your room, feel lost and miserable if you like, but obey me. That is his power; he can afford to let me feel whatever I want, as long as I go up to my room. So this explanation I am going to give you is why I fear the dream of going back upstairs in our old house in Budapest, to the room that looks out over the roofs of other houses, it is so high up; it looks out on the sky and the clouds and later out on the night lights. The night lights twinkle on and off, strong and weak, in no fixed pattern, so that you could explore them forever, throughout the night, in the room to which you have obediently retreated.

A priest who thought he was enlightened once said to me, "I tell young men troubled by dreams about other young men to go marry; it is a holy state, and one warm

body is much like another in bed." I consider this priest
of the demon's party. If it were true that all warm bodies
are much the same, if skin, bone, and the texture of hair
had no particular sense attached to one person rather
than another, then we should have no particular reason
to live. One day is much like the next, isn't it? And since
they are all the same, it doesn't matter how many of them
there are, does it? You see how the priest gives a counsel
of despair. It is only when I decide that a nipple matters
to me because it pushes up from the hard, hairy chest of
a man rather than the soft bosom of a woman, only when
I decide this particular fact matters that I want to live.

You understand, I am not making an argument for
the superiority of my particular tastes. When I was young
I thought, this particular taste of mine is the reason why
I am so unhappy. I did not feel guilty about my men, a
fact I do not comprehend but which appears to me rather
in the character of a miraculous escape. Not guilty, but
I thought that, like a kaleidoscope, my loving would re-
compose itself in more normal ways once I was happy.
Then later I thought: I will continue my particular tastes
until I must settle down. And then, after my father died,
I thought: It doesn't matter, I will go on as I have been.
But at none of these points did I say: This love is the
love I want. The point I am trying to make is that I was
floating through life. As a boy, when I went to my room,
my mind sought out abstract thoughts for relief, floating
thoughts, and so you see what I mean about not going
back to my room, and this is one reason why I do not want
you back, Natalie, because I do not want the particular
physical thing which is you. To live is to love something
concrete for itself.

A War Diary

The war has forced me to acknowledge what I was too comfortable in my room of sorrows and dreams to face. How easily time passed there. In a war, dreaming is dangerous to others, and usually fatal to oneself. It has been a terrible discipline to pay attention only to the present, but it has taught me, an unwilling pupil, some simple facts.

For instance, while nothing will ever cause me to believe in a god, I have become a Jew. The Russian people, as I often pointed out to you, hate Jews. It struck me when I came to this country that the Communist regime, no less than the Tsars, knew how to manipulate this hatred so as to deflect people from thinking about the miseries imposed by the government. And, in the years 1933 to 1941, I saw in Russia exact copies of the raids against Jews in Germany. Jews who had shops were attacked by young men and women—I call your attention to that fact, pregnant young girls in babushkas throwing stones at shopwindows as though they were getting some snowball exercise—Jews were attacked by these young people while the police stood by, bored, often chewing pieces of horse fat to keep warm. The Party got into the act when the attack was then reported in the press. "Black Market profiteer brought to justice by the People," *Pravda* would report. "The shop of X, who has been known to sell controlled goods on the sly, finally so incensed the residents of such and such district that they took the law into their hands and drove the profiteer out of business." Now the sentence of genius would be put in: "Unfortunately, X belongs to a race long noted for its love of money."

What is the purpose of such a sentence? After all, so many Party members were themselves Jews. There you have it exactly—so many Party members were themselves Jews. Make a man ashamed and you make him your servant. Jews are money hungry; Communism is a war waged on behalf of simple, pure people against money-hungry persons; ergo, a Jewish Communist is by definition at war with himself. I seldom heard Party Jews in the prewar years protest against these sentences published by *Pravda*. No, they were uncomfortable. Discipline through shame: a formula showing the genius of our Party.

Of course, the wild attacks on Jews in those prewar years also gave the simple, pure, noble Russian people relief from their troubles, relief which they had sought since time immemorial under the Tsars. Your noble average man blamed the Jews, in particular, for the lack of consumer goods. The Jews were hoarding shoes, butter, cream, and buttons. In those days I had not yet learned to savor life's little ironies. It enraged me that the Party should encourage people to believe that their own greedy desires were being defeated by "class enemies." I will, moreover, say that this policy of encouraging attacks on elderly Jewish men and women, this drawing of hammers-and-sickles on the walls of synagogues, gave people in those years the feeling that they were still fighting for something. This was particularly true of the younger pure, simple, and noble Russians. In stoning Jew-hoarders, they could believe they were part of the Great Revolution, a second generation of heroes.

Now, many persons, including myself, expected the war against the Germans to curb the tide of hatred against Jews on the part of the Russian people. But not at all. The Jews are responsible for the war! If they did not exist, then the Germans would not be fighting, ravaging, pillaging, and destroying. In my travels over the last few years, I have heard versions of this explanation of the war over and over again. I should say that, if anything, hatred against the Jews has become worse; we are fighting to protect these peddlers of bread and buttons?

All this has put me on the alert. Russia needs her Jews; otherwise, there would be no one the older generation could blame for misery, and the younger generation would be deprived of its idealistic desire to continue the revolutionary struggle. Everyone would be without an explanation. So this profound need of the Russian people for Jews has forced me to see that I am enrolled in the race of my ancestors, whether I like it or not, because I am needed to swell the ranks of Jews, who are constantly dying out. I am now on the alert for what my fellow comrades will make of this identity they have forced upon me. That is what I mean, by saying I must pay attention to the present.

But, Tibor, you will say, we cannot leave it go at this. What about the important thing? You have not told me what happened after we were divorced. Was there someone else? And my answer to this question is: no, there has been no one else, but if he appears, I hope I am ready. What I am trying to say—which perhaps contradicts all my fine strictures on love—is that in the meantime the possibility I will find him is not the only thing. I cannot just wait for love. I also have to make sure I am alive tomorrow night.

July . . . These experiences with gas have something to do with the verb "to exist." Last week, a little girl was trapped on the second story of a building, after a bomb dropped clear through a coal shute in the basement and exploded. Fortunately, the bomb was small, and we had plenty of time to set up our ladders to get to the girl. They ordered me to serve as controller of the collection of small-sized gas masks for section 6 of Vlinka last week, so it was I who took one up with me on the ladder to give to the little girl. Now imagine her fright, in a burning building, smoke everywhere below her, when a man appears, looking like some sort of horrible metal insect, and speaking through the distorting filter of the mask. She ran away from me! Toward the fire! I couldn't take off my mask on the ladder safely, so I just had to jump through the window and run after her. I caught her and, to her horror, began strapping an insect around her face. She was coughing from the gas now seeping up into the second story, and yet she kept trying to take off her mask. I had to hold her hands behind her back while she kicked at my legs, trying to escape me and remove the loathsome insect mask. Finally, I retreated with her in my arms out of the window and down the ladder.

Earlier this spring, I was helping four people fight a fire started by a gas bomb in a park outside Minsk. The flames cut me off from them at one point, and I suddenly went into a panic, imagining I was imprisoned by walls of flame all around me. You have heard of the panic reactions of soldiers in battle, like shitting in their pants, or suddenly jumping up in a foxhole and waving their arms to the enemy, begging to be killed. I had such a moment of panic then, and I took off my mask.

Was there still poison gas in the air? I was afraid to breathe. I stood helpless and terrified, with my hand over my mouth, thinking I must not inhale a molecule. And then finally I couldn't hold out and gasped in a big breath of air—and there was no gas. But then I thought—my panic migrating—well, I don't know if there is gas because maybe it is odorless, and the only way I will know is by breathing more, but I will die proving there is gas in the air. My panic ended; I put on my mask.

I can hear Piotr now: Does this not prove, Tibor, that breathing mediates between subject and object? That the body measures the philosophical distinction? Such an intelligent boy, and so good. But I would say to him, I think, that I simply am filled with awe at these events. The little girl could have died out of fear; I could have died out of either fear or curiosity. These are risks with existence, and yet, if she had no fear, if I had no curiosity, we would be dead in another way. It reminds me of that childhood argument with Aunt Doreen; I would not believe her when she explained about the hibernation of bears. I couldn't imagine a bear living without his daily amble through the forest; an afternoon rest after a fish lunch perhaps, but a bear without movement and yet alive? This is why I insisted on taking Henry, my stuffed brown bear, out for a stroll every day, in order that he would not suffer from the hibernation Aunt Doreen described. So my answer to Piotr would be that these experiences about gas prove that hibernating is not existing. But the answer would be meaningless to Piotr, because he was never in danger of hibernation. I was.

Today: Nine prisoners interviewed. Nothing of interest from them; now they must be disposed of. The weekly dispatch said there would be a train at the branch station today at 13:00 with a cattle car for prisoners. We marched the prisoners to the station platform, but there was no train at 13:00. Or 14:00. Or at 15:00. Lunch was

The Frog Who Dared to Croak

a dozen potatoes for six guards, nothing for the prisoners. I kept up morale by telling a story. The Germans have no books of any sort in their kits. I asked them if I should make up a story for them in their own language. They said yes eagerly, and as I told my tale, many of them began to sleep, lulled by the rhythm of familiar words in a wasteland where no one understands their cries, their pleading, or their dreams.

I told the story of the Transylvanian frogs, and I told it this way. I said that once upon a time there lived in Transylvania a group of frogs. They were athletes, high jumpers, who went each summer to a training camp in the mountains. I said that these frogs became enormously proud of themselves; they felt contempt for other frogs who could not jump as high as they could. One of the prisoners, a young boy, commented, "Yes, yes, it must always be like that." His masters had schooled him well.

The Transylvanian frogs, I continued, spent ever more time at their training camp, practicing jumping. They had a goal, the all-animal Olympics where they would compete against teams of frogs from throughout the world. The winning team would then compete in an all-animal jump; if the frog could jump straight up five times its own height in the air, for instance, it would win over a cat which could jump straight up only four times its height. Another soldier asked me how a frog could ever hope to best a cat; his comrades told him to be quiet. They wanted the story, any story, and also, I think, they were afraid to make a captor angry by asking questions.

I said that, in the training camp in the mountains, the frogs became ever better athletes, and I described in great detail their exercises, since this seemed to interest the two or three prisoners paying attention—I

A *War Diary*

described how the high-jump bar was raised a few centi-
meters every day, which stretching exercises the frogs
performed, the martial songs the frogs sang. All this
made sense to my listeners, as I had hoped, because they
must have been put through a similar training.

And then I talked about the consequences of that
contempt the frogs felt for others who were not strong.
I said that on the paths of the mountain retreat, when
the frogs encountered an old toad or a tortoise, they would
jump up and down, shouting abuse and laughing, so that
the toad would become afraid, or the tortoise would with-
draw into its shell. Once the frogs even turned over an
old tortoise in its shell onto its back, and the tortoise
would have died in a terrible, dizzy agony had not some
friendly beavers come by and gently put it upright. I made
no comment on this aggressiveness of the young frogs.

At last, I said, the great event came, the all-animal
Olympics. For two years the frogs had been training.
They were amazing, hopping and flipping in ways no one
had ever seen the like of before. They strutted around
Rome, the site of the games, as though they had already
won all the medals. And at the first set of trials, their
arrogance did not seem misplaced. They easily beat the
frogs from other countries; they were so good that the
crowd swelled every time one of them was to perform and
dwindled away as soon as a competitor appeared. There
was no question about the outcome.

But then they began their comparative trial with
members of other species—here I interrupted the story
to explain the rules of proportion and handicapping to
the German soldier who had initially asked the question.
He had fallen asleep, but for the sake of my story, I woke
him up. He understood not a word—and at these com-

parative trials things went another way. A cat from Sweden won the straight jump against the most junior member of the Transylvanian frogs. But then a more senior frog won the jump across against a Mexican rabbit. The score was one to one; the frogs spoke bitterly to their junior member for having lost, and he was utterly crushed; yet a third event was to come, one which pitted the frog team captain against a black cat, and so victory was still possible. (I thought this was good: black should make my listeners think of the boxing match in the 1936 Olympics, but I didn't make the thing too obvious by saying the black cat came from America.) It was a jump-and-somersault contest, the frog captain's specialty. He went first. He made a fantastic leap up and forward, did a double somersault, and ended squarely on his feet. It was beautiful, and broke the Olympic record for frogs. But then the black cat stepped to the jumping line and, like an airplane, sailed up and forward, did a triple somersault, and broke the world Olympic record for cats by a much greater margin than the frog did for his species. The crowd was stunned: silence, then an immense roar of applause, and the frogs, earlier fêted throughout Rome, were jeered at or, worse, simply ignored, as arrogant losers who had received their comeuppance.

Among the German prisoners, only the young boy was still paying attention, and it was a pity, since now I had reached the point of my story. The frogs returned embittered and disgraced to Transylvania. They expected more of the scorn they experienced in Rome at home, and as soon as they could, went straight back to their training camp in the mountains, to avoid animals in the city. Here they were surprised. Neither the toad nor even the tortoise they had almost killed made fun of them. No, not at all. There was some coolness at first, but gradually the toad spoke consoling words to them; the young frog member of the team, who had always felt bad about the tortoise incident, happened to be able to help the old creature across a bridge one day, and was invited home to tea. Most surprisingly, the frogs, in this atmosphere of harmony bred of failure in the world, began to have a new interest in their jumping. They began to take pleasure in flipping, hopping, and jump-across just to feel the muscles in their body move—the sheer pleasure, the art even, of movement.

The moral of this story, I concluded, is that true happiness comes not from mastery of others but from fraternity. Only in a world of brothers can an animal or a man take pleasure in himself. My last words were, "Real fraternity occurs among those who share their frailties."

The young German prisoner looked at me for a moment. Then he shrugged. "But all that cannot be real." At this point, the train we had so long been waiting for came into the station. Our platoon formed guard alert; the other prisoners woke up. We marched them to the gates of the cattle car; the gates were unlocked. The prisoners climbed up one by one into the empty interior smelling of cow. I locked the gates behind them, the train pulled slowly out of the station, and we walked in the dusk back to our quarters.

(Undated): The closer we come to the Hungarian border, the closer we come to . . . I met Bartha yesterday at a meeting of interrogators. He is an old Hungarian revolutionary; the war has not been too bad for him, although he is very thin. After the meeting we went to the edge of a wood and sat, perched on the back of a truck, talking about the old days. We spoke in Hungarian.

I told Bartha I was at once desperate and afraid to set foot again in my native land. He simply didn't understand this.

"Bartha," I said, "you and I have a similar life. A turbulent youth. Exile to the East. The travesty here of all we once believed. But among our own people, don't you think it still would be possible? We only had a few weeks, we weren't really given a chance."

"You still believe what you did as a younger man?" Bartha asked me incredulously. "Papa Marx and all that?"

"No, certainly not. But remember those families forced to live in the Municipal Park, remember the food riots when the garbage cans from good houses were emptied? No, I am saying that if we go back, one has to prevent life from becoming again this old misery. Or at least, I say, one has to want to prevent it, one has to want something more than just surviving. And, moreover, in our country I believe it is possible."

"My dear Tibor, what a pretty speech," Barku commented.

This made me angry; I do not like people to be ironic. I fell silent.

I remembered Bartha well from the days of the Hungarian Revolution. He worked in a prosaic but important post, in the Department of Public Sanitation. We had numerous health problems, then, due to the condition of the public lavatories, as well as the public baths, which were often no more than *pissoirs*. While most bourgeois revolutionaries felt a certain embarrassment about confronting such matters, Bartha, who came from a very

A War Diary

grand family, was absolutely straightforward and brisk about them. He would give demonstrations in the public lavatories on the correct use of the mechanisms, something the immigrant peasants had never had to learn in the country and no one in the old regime had ever cared to show them. For instance, they had to be told why a flush toilet is not like a well. Bartha also explained the use of toilet paper, and its medical advantages, even dropping his trousers, once when I attended one of his classes, to show exactly how the tissues should be handled. It must be remembered that excrement, in a remote peasant community, is not considered disgusting; it is a valuable substance. It is conserved and graded according to its quality, used either as fertilizer or in making bricks. This means it is constantly touched by human hands. Bartha's job was to convince peasants who had moved to Budapest that they must change their ideas about excrement. In the city, it was no longer to be treated so familiarly and directly; it was to be treated as dangerous. Bartha liked to say, "My classes are their first step on the road to a life of lace doilies."

To me now he said, "Since you always like stories, Tibor, let me tell you one. When supplies ran low in 1942, Our Leader in Minsk decided on an emergency rationing system. A clever man, he thought it up all by himself. The Party members got first crack at potatoes, bread, rice, coal, and so on. The higher up in the Party, the larger one's ration. Our Leader said that if, God forbid, starvation should set in, the most valuable people, that is, the leaders, should be kept alive. This is for the good of everyone, in the end. Now it so happened that in Minsk there were many Party members who were also professional soldiers of the old school, some even trained in

The Frog Who Dared to Croak

Germany. These tough old birds had a different idea. A leader takes care of his men, so the men should be fed first; a leader is a leader because he is willing to take more privation.

"Well, one night in the winter of 1942, secret police went to the military barracks and arrested these officers for giving food to the troops. The officers were taken to prison, and shot two days later as subversives. What is interesting about the story is the reaction of the men. On the whole, they approved of the 'disappearance,' as it was officially called. Ordinary soldiers, cold and ragged, were uncomfortable eating when their superiors in fine uniforms drank water and nibbled potato peelings. This wasn't right. Now, I find this a very inspiring story, indeed, about how the ideals of the Communist Party can spread down to the lowest ranks of society."

I stood up to leave. I said I didn't need such lessons.

"Oh, my dear fellow, but you do. Have you not told me the war has changed your life? Like all too many cynics, you have been lying in wait to believe, when only the right event or the right belief or the right time and place comes along. Now, I am not cynical at all, not at all. I simply take life at its true measure.

"Isn't it strange how phrases can be corrupted and still retain some shred of meaning. For instance, when you are at a café late at night with a woman, you may say something like, 'I am afraid I am falling in love with you.' You are not falling in love; you are simply aroused. You certainly are not afraid of falling into bed with this beauty; you hope to tumble. A cunning phrase, though; it expresses a truth about our desires, which is that they are frightening, and the woman, if she is worthy of you, will both see through the remark and appreciate it. Now, just as it is with desire, so it is with power. Our great Communist Party has made a mockery of words like 'freedom' and 'enemies,' yet the language of oppression that the workers speak at rallies, at Marx-study classes, thinking it makes them free now, indicates as though by an echo, by a trace in memory, a time and a place in which saying the words 'class warfare' meant defiance of a reality, and so had a meaning as war."

I had no idea where Bartha was leading me.

"You, Tibor, have always been too timid in love. I've observed this ever since you were a boy. You could have had women panting after you if only you weren't so shy, which is to say if you didn't make a kiss such an important event. It is exactly the same problem you are now having about going home. My dear fellow, it just doesn't matter. My life is an endless series of mistakes. Why should the life of ten million people together be any different? Why should it matter to get it right more in one part of the globe than in any other? I am serious now, my friend."

There was no logical answer to this, for Bartha was no demon like the priest. We began to discuss more practical matters. Bartha said he believed that both the capitalist powers and Russia would fight for territory in Hungary, Czechoslovakia, and Poland, once the Germans were destroyed; there would be no effort, as after the First World War, to create neutral states. I agreed with this, saying neutrality was in any case an illusion when the world was ruled by great powers. "You see, you see," Bartha exclaimed, "no place is sacred, virginal, alone. Countries, like the people in them, are always fucking." I steered to even more immediate matters. Bartha now revealed that he, too, will make every effort to be posted to Hungary, once we cross the border. He has heard that the Hungarians have only just begun to mobilize for defense against us, which seems incredible to me, but that is the way of a land-locked country ruled by an admiral for over twenty years. At the end of our talk, Bartha offered to get me a place in his intelligence unit, if he could.

(Undated): At last we have arrived at the frontier. At Beregovo. There is a huge mass of refugees here—Poles, Hungarians, Belorussians, Georgians. As usual, the authorities routed many more people to a place than it can possibly accommodate. Barku is here, directing work on an open latrine system behind the refugee camps. My *capitaine* has commandeered the best house in town. Every day at 1400, refugees crowd around the railroad station, when orders come over the telegraph about future resettlement movements. There is a holding camp for some German prisoners. I can do no work with them, because we are constantly having to move them from hut to hut to protect them from the refugees, who want blood. To his great credit, the adjutant has ordered that there be no trials without proper interrogation and case preparation; in any event, the German boys know nothing. This, of course, will not prevent them from being held responsible for everything. The Hungarians tell the most depressing stories about the Horthy regime, the Poles the same about the Germans. Everyone wants to go home. The war is over, as far as these people are concerned, the moment they can get back into their houses. Yet, week after week, no news comes for them of when they will be allowed to cross the borders.

This morning, there was a meeting of the few surviving Jews, those from the Beregovo region plus those who are here as refugees, military personnel, civilian administrators. We met in the synagogue on Vigilance Against Counterrevolutionaries Street. "Synagogue" means three walls without a roof. Time and war dust have erased the slogans painted on the walls during the war. "Synagogue" means a memory. The chief rabbi burned the chairs for fuel during the winter months of 1942. By 1943 he had disappeared, but a lesser rabbi had burned in the winter of 1943 the wooden scroll screen behind which the women sat; the women's benches are also gone. Then everyone was deported. The Torah was hidden when the Germans first threatened the town, but none of these survivors know where.

We were a motley group. It was my second time in a synagogue in my entire life, and I believe many of the other officers and Party functionaries who were there had also had no previous contact with their religion. We feel daring in entering an opium den of the masses, but not too daring. This month, at least, it is a mark of honor to be Jewish, the Party believing this month that the enemy of my enemy is my friend. The old ones who kept the faith are in despair. Their road map has been erased. They look at the place where the women's screen used to be; they peer into some special cabinet or crypt where the Torah was kept. All they see is absence. The old women by habit take their places behind the invisible screen; a young woman, a Party woman, comes down to the front to stand among the men. The old ones avert their eyes.

Never in my life have I prayed. Certainly, I have wished for magical changes in life—the triumph of my great plans in 1919; a slow, immensely painful, untreatable disease to be visited on the Minsk Officer of Ideo-

The Frog Who Dared to Croak

logical Standards, a book of Proust suddenly placed in my hands while on fire duty in Vlinka. We all have such desires. But that I should actually address myself to a being made of air, whose only claims to existence lie in that appalling record of barbarism and cruelty called the Old Testament, that I should pray to this God for help is unthinkable. Yet this morning, I was obscurely hoping, without admitting the thought to myself, that we should pray.

This proved impossible. The old ones refused. There was no rabbi, no book, no screen, hats were not acceptable substitutes for skullcaps. And only the old ones knew the words of prayer. So, instead, we stood and talked.

We talked of the two ways opening up before us, the way of sacrifice in the pursuit of truth, and the way of survival. For us, this is the difference between death and life. The Hungarian and the Italian were discussing a somewhat different problem: the way of sacrifice in the pursuit of beauty, and the way of beauty surviving. If for one moment I or any other human being in Russia had yielded to an aesthetic reaction to the war, we would have gone mad. I know this is what the bourgeois artists in the West do. They seek the exact color of blood in paintings, or they make ever so beautiful sentences which evoke shrapnel smearing bodies in a foxhole. We talked about those who refused to be led to the train station, and the surviving ones, those who hid. Why did my dear frogs learn about charity, and we discuss the truths of breathing yet another day? Consider the evidence: do real frogs kill for the sake of affirming free froghood? Man is the animal who thinks.

Bartha would say that the synagogue has put me in a preachy mood. If I were to set down my conversation with the old men and women in exact detail, however, he would probably be bored. Who was taken away on December 14, who on the fifteenth; how Mrs. X hid behind the coal shute for a week, how Mrs. Y dyed her hair to avoid being detected; the rough way the police led old Mr. Z out of the house. I suppose this enumeration of the details of disappearance, this census of loss, was our manner of praying.

Part Five

The Frog
Croaks

14

This document consists of four texts in Hungarian, with comments by Grau in German. The document is in excellent physical condition.

They say old people are prisoners of habit. But what "they" do not understand is that life will not leave us alone.

I returned to Hungary after the war. Without the war's excitements, my vitality ebbed. It was only natural; many others have told me they felt themselves sinking back into old habits once danger was past. In some ways, however, my life had been ineradicably altered. For one thing, my books had begun to appear abroad. In the unsettled conditions of Hungary, a writer with an international reputation was considered by the authorities an asset, someone who gave the country prestige and drew people's attention away from the collaboration of the Hungarians with the Nazis. So I was given certain privileges: a chair at the university, a private flat, and, most valuable of all, occasional permission to travel abroad.

These visits, especially one to England, helped me see that the changes I thought the war had wrought in my character were incomplete. In 1948 I gave a lecture at

Oxford. I had nothing to fear from the philosophy students because their minds were anesthetized, occupied
with the meaning of prepositions and pronouns and similar matters best left to poets. I had only to fear the resi-
dent K.G.B. agent sent from home, whom I spotted
instantly, thanks to my long training in such matters.
And yet, even so, I spoke more cautiously than I would
have at home. In London I did meet people with blood in
their veins, who had ideas, who welcomed me, and yet
also with these people I was careful.

Upon my return, I pondered this. Caution is a disease
of the mind, and I was chronically ill. Yet in my case
the disease was not fatal. I could not re-create the stim-
ulus of war, even if I wanted to, but at least I could think
and teach in a way that did not irritate the fibers of my
disease. So I decided to teach about old thinkers and old
thoughts, Aquinas, Plato, Boethius, people of whom one
could speak forthrightly because they were long dead.

The lectures I began to give in 1949 must have given
pleasure, because many people attended them, not just
young students but ex-soldiers in wheelchairs, middle-
aged ladies, even my concierge. Probably nothing made
sense to them—save the pleasure of hearing someone
talk openly and naturally, simply hearing a warm voice.
When I lectured in Russia before the war, I had to shout
propaganda as loudly as I could at strategic moments
during the lecture; a policeman at the back of the hall
checked my words against his text of what one should
be saying that day. My old thinkers did not matter enough
for such surveillance.

It was at one of these lectures that I found great joy
in a love that came to me late in life, but it did come, and
for it the war prepared me. He is an older man, also Hun-

The Frog Croaks

garian, who was wounded by the Nazis in 1943. He invited me to tea after one of my best talks—on Plato's fable of the cave. I helped him home on his crutches, and that very night we made love. Two old men kissing and hugging each other. My friend is an accountant—he reminds me of the man named Goldstein whom I knew many years ago during the Hungarian Soviet. He also reminds me of my former wife, Natalie; or rather, her emotional vulnerability is replaced by his physical vulnerability. But I do not attack him. My friend came to live with me as a companion in the flat, and I now feel useful to some other human being in washing him, helping him dress, and reading to him when the shrapnel embedded inside him makes it too painful for him to read himself. I know what you will say: Grau, such a self-absorbed, unpleasant man before, now redeemed. You really understand nothing. I simply have something to do. This life has formed for me those habits of small pleasures each day which the young would call the prison of old age. So different a prison, if it is, than my room at the top of my family's house.

The story I must tell is of the test events finally made of this life, a life in which I believed I had reached an understanding with my disease. Although, thanks to my work and my friend, I was content, the country was not. All our old devils stole back after the peace: strife between the ethnic groups, between political factions, between the rich and the poor. We were captives of the Russians, but their own problems were so great that our country suffered more from anarchy than despotism. It was inevitable that the people would grow restless; they did. By the fall of 1956, they were so miserable that they revolted.

Outsiders can have no appreciation, I believe, of how confusing things were then. On October 23, the National Radio Building was seized by the insurgents. The next day Russian troops moved into Budapest; wild street fighting broke out. It seemed to me this would be the end of the uprising, but panic and rage in the city had created their own momentum. On the twenty-fifth of October, the Hungarian Secret Police, the A.V.O., killed six hundred people in Parliament Square; that afternoon, the Russians decided to change the Party leadership from the hated Gero to János Kádár, a relatively unknown man. For some reason, this change only stirred up the people of Budapest to new fury. Kádár promised more changes in the Party if only the people would calm themselves. On October 30, the A.V.O. police, trapped within Party headquarters, ran out of ammunition. They surrendered, and I was on the edge of the crowd when they did. As they came out of the Party building in small groups, the insurgents butchered them. I saw the leader of the A.V.O., Imre Mezo, shot dead as he walked out of the building carrying a white flag. The Russians responded that night by firing on a hospital or a school, I don't know which.

On October 29, before the killing of the A.V.O. police and the bombing of the hospital or school, it was decided that six prominent Hungarians would meet with the Russian political attaché Yuri Stos. The events of October 30 made this meeting, a rare contact between Hungarians and the U.S.S.R. government outside Party channels, ever more pressing, and it was arranged for the morning of November 1.

I was one of the six. Because I was well known, I was chosen; because I was retiring, the others thought I would go along with whatever the meeting decided. I saw in this meeting the possibility I would be tested. I was. The night before the discussion was scheduled, the Hungarians came to me and said that they would urge the Russians to allow Hungary to become a neutral socialist regime, like Yugoslavia. They believed that, because of my sufferings under Stalin, I would concur. I did not. I believe the very idea of neutrality in the world of great powers is an illusion, and I told my fellow Hungarians so. I had an alternative proposal.

I wrote down my thoughts, after they left, hoping that someday they would be published. At the meeting with the Russians, I repeated these remarks in a summary form, and to the extent prudence permitted.

Gentlemen:

This is a terrible and glorious day in our history. The people of Hungary have declared their determination to control their own destiny. But they must fill their mouths with blood to do so. I direct myself to those of you who think blood is good to drink. I want the violence to stop; the only way for it to stop is if we come to an understanding with the Russians.

I shall make three points. First, we will never succeed in becoming neutral. The Russians won't allow it, and, pursuing this goal, we will live in endless civil war. Two, the goal is an illusion. To be neutral is not to exist; everyone is forced in life to take sides. Three, there is very little we can gain from the West, particularly the Americans. If we were to succeed through great bloodshed in achieving that illusionary state of neutrality, we would in fact simply become the servant of two masters.

I hope you will heed my words, because I have lived through something like these days once before in Hungary. I am the oldest person in this room; I want to convince you of your foolishness, because in 1919 I was foolish, too.

To understand my three points, I would like you to consider the old meaning of the word "revolution." The word described the circling of the sun around the earth. A revolution implied not change but seasonal order; at the end of each year, the sun returned to the place in which it began. We—I speak to the Hungarians—have experienced revolution in this ancient sense. We have revolved, too, seeking to escape the tyrannical center. But, like a captive sun, we change where we are in our historical orbit but never get farther away.

A recent fact will make the image clear. There was a rash of "accidental" fires on collective farms earlier this year. The fires occurred in haystacks. The rural police gave extra training in fire control, the fools. I knew from 1919 what the meaning of these fires was. Starve the animals, kill the crops, and one strikes a blow against the state! Here we have people burning up their lives to punish their masters. Hence I speak of our Revolution being a revolution in the antique mode. Do you not see that the heat released by those burning haystacks is orbital revolutionary energy?

Let me proceed to the first of my three points about this Revolution of ours. We could tire the Russians out militarily if they were tired in other ways. But they have not yet exhausted their ideas about themselves. The Khrushchev revelations earlier this year have not weakened the socialist system of our neighbor. Far from it. The tyranny of the old order was unmasked, and this unmasking gave men previously in the shadows the right to hold power. These Russians have a new lease on life.

The Frog Croaks

This, I assure you, will not put them in a mood to tolerate a similar new lease on life for others.

Consider a historical contrast. In the last days of the Roman Empire, both the people and the emperors were fatigued. People dressed in barbarian clothes at fancy-dress balls, barbarian food became chic at Roman banquets, the rulers of the world were so tired of their own ways that they thought it amusing, ironic, to ape the manners of the tribes bent on destroying them. At a particularly debauched gladiatorial combat in the Forum, the people actually cheered the unarmed Ostrogoths fighting the armed Romans. Such are the conditions under which a giant power releases its hold on its possessions. These are not the conditions which prevail today in Moscow.

In 1919, I heard very often, especially from Béla Kun, the argument that, though the oppressors had the might, a people armed with the will to liberty could always find ingenious ways of going "around" that might. Kun cited as an example the glass bottle. In 1919, as in the last month, this wondrous object revealed to us its virtues. A prudent man can litter the streets with broken bottles, causing, in 1919, the feet of horses to bleed, and in 1956, the tires of police cars to bust. A brave man can fill a glass bottle with brandy or petrol, insert a rag wick, light it, and throw a bomb into the police van. A desperate man can fight policemen hand to hand with a broken bottle. When a shortage of glass bottles began to develop this year, I knew something serious was up. I take such a sign far more seriously, in truth, than all the theses written by my students on ripening infrastructural conditions and dialectical contradictions. Today, as thirty-seven years ago, the authorities were blind. They actually increased

The Frog Who Dared to Croak

production of glass bottles to make up for this mysterious shortage.

Very good, but, gentlemen, a war conducted with glass bottles is a war of gestures. A police car explodes. The police, in retaliation, may destroy the entire population of the village in which it exploded. Each of you in this room can think of examples during the recent war when the Fascists used such counterterror. Kun was wrong. Power is not a stone which one goes around or at which one chips away. It is a whole system, and the only way power can be changed is, as with the Romans, when the oppressors find themselves ludicrous.

This is why the violence in our country must stop. The historical moment is not right; rebellious acts will lead to ever more massive acts of retaliation; the only result will be the devastation of our country. But, you will say, these people in the streets are not blind. They have a purpose, which is to create a neutral status for our country.

This, I say to you, is the pursuit of an illusion. I say that to be neutral is not to exist.

Consider the animal kingdom, consider the frogs, for example. Frogs seem like peaceful creatures. Without teeth, consuming only the most inoffensive algae, they seem to live in a neutral state in nature. But, in fact, they are only pawns in the struggle for life in a pond. Their flesh provides the meat for animals with teeth, who, strengthened on a diet of frogs, do battle with one another for dominance—the snake, the rat. The frog's only weapon of survival is his sperm. He breeds so many millions of his kind that a few in each generation remain after the other animals have sated their hunger. This is what it means to be truly neutral.

The Frog Croaks

Gentlemen, we simply do not breed fast enough to achieve the neutrality of the defenseless frogs. Our children are few and undernourished; to survive, they must have protectors. Yes, our protectors are demanding.

This brings me to my third point. Neutral means more open to the West, or, as I say, open to serving two masters rather than one. What would the new rulers be like?

You have only to look at the events of recent weeks to become suspicious of the friendship America offers. For the last eight years, the propaganda organs of America have broadcast radio programs to our people inciting them to arise, to shake off the shackles of Communism. Very well, we are now trying at least to shake off Russian shackles. Where is the support of the Americans in our hour of need? Have they sent troops, have they put real pressures on our Russian masters to stop the tanks? Of course not.

After all, this should not surprise us. Power is power. I do not blame these Americans, who have encouraged our people to expect help and then have done nothing. We are pawns in a game of power, and why should they have any interest in us other than as pawns. No, I simply say that, for us, we must recognize that we are small, that we must act cunningly, craftily from our position of pawnhood. To imagine we can escape from a pawn's orbit, when our only weapons are rage and broken glass bottles, this is lunacy.

These are my three points. We cannot win an armed struggle; there is no such thing as neutrality; if we could somehow become freer from Russia, we would end up serving both Russia and America. The result of serving two warring masters is that we would be destroyed.

I shall close my speech with a final, and most im-

The Frog Who Dared to Croak

portant, observation. It concerns our Russian masters. Is there anyone in this room who imagines I love them? But it is not only the Russians who are at fault. Our movement has failed to ripen. Even if there were no Russians, we speak a language which would lead us to enslave ourselves. Much has been done: people no longer sleep in trees, diseases are treated, but we still are plagued by our thoughts.

Especially because we are Hungarians, we are too comfortable with the condition of being desperate. Consider what went on in the Municipal Park this summer. A truck with a loudspeaker mounted on top would drive slowly through the park, blaring out some propagandistic garbage, a message which no one could make out, moreover, because the sound systems are always faulty on these vehicles. After it passed, strangers—mind you, total strangers—would turn to each other and smile. Imagine people so brave and so desperate as to smile at one another in the wake of a propaganda message. Yet this desperation, can it suffice as a way of life?

I am a realist, I believe in survival. Also, I know that the events of the last weeks, if they are dealt with intelligently, can be used to make our lives better, if not good. We must turn matters to account so that the Russians give us specific realms of autonomy. For instance, we must change the manner in which the Party is structured; we must give local units, unions, collectives, cities, more flexibility. In return for this, we should agree to maintain appearances, to swear fealty to them. This is the sort of practical work we can at this moment do. Better terms with the masters, that is what will save us, rather than the dream of being masterless.

The Frog Croaks

Such were my words. They made no difference. János Kádár spoke harshly to Stos. Stos said that either the Hungarians break the back of the violence or the U.S.S.R. would. Stos was uninterested in my ideas about a negotiation over new military, economic, and political terms between the two countries. Events had passed us by. The Hungarian people continued to struggle in the first week of November 1956; the Russians in a massive show of force overwhelmed them. János Kádár, brought into power as a moderate, survived by becoming a spokesman for the Russian masters. The smile hardened on Khrushchev's face.

You would have thought that the news of my speech, which inevitably spread, would have brought me new honor among my countrymen. For a few days, it did. But then, as people knuckled under to the old ways, an entirely predictable reversal occurred. It was said that I spoke against my fellow Hungarians during the time of troubles, it was said by people anxious to lick the master's boots but anxious also to maintain the myth of their own probity. I became a scapegoat. The first tangible sign of my new status came to me in a published report of the Ethnic Minorities Section of the Hungarian Party. Here it is:

February 18, 1957
Ethnic Minorities Section
Hungarian Communist Party

On February 16, this section held its monthly meeting. Item 6 on the agenda concerned the behavior of Comrade Tibor Grau during the events of October–November in 1956. Specifically, charges were brought against the said

Comrade Grau the seriousness of which suggest he be barred from further membership in the Hungarian Communist Party. These charges are as follows:

1. On October 23, he was seen by three other Ethnic Minorities Section members to observe a conflict between lawful police authorities and counterrevolutionaries outside the Mathias Church. Grau stood passively by, making no attempt to aid the authorities.
2. On October 25, he was seen by three other Ethnic Minorities Section members coming out of St. Stephen's Basilica after an illegal religious ceremony in that building. His expression was such that the members concluded he had been engaged in an act of religious worship.
3. On October 26, he was seen entering the Academia church, near the law faculty.
4. On October 26, he was seen and spoken to by an Ethnic Minorities Section comrade on a bench by the citadel. Comrade Grau was reading a book of fairy tales by the German author Grimm. When asked by the comrade why he was reading this book at such a moment, with the city disturbed by hooligan elements, he replied, "It helps me keep my sense of reality."
5. It is known that Comrade Grau made a speech on November 1 in the presence of our Russian political attaché and colleague, Comrade Stos. Many stories have since circulated, on good authority, about the content of this speech. Specifically, Comrade Grau must:
   a. Answer the charge that he used a metaphor that implied Hungary was the "captive" of the Soviet

Union. The Hungarian Communist Party Central Committee has made it officially known that without the assistance of our Russian comrades, the counterrevolutionary and hooligan forces in this country would have gravely damaged the Revolution. To be sure, it is also officially established that the cult of personality practiced in an earlier phase of the Revolution did create grave problems. However, these problems were of an organizational character throughout the socialist world. Were Comrade Grau to have alleged that the people were "captive" of certain political elements during the period of the cult of personality, this metaphor might conceivably be just. However, to imply that there is a "national element of captivity" is not permissible. The Ethnic Minorities Section is particularly concerned about this charge, because one of the achievements of the socialist revolution since the last world war has been to overcome regional and ethnic hostilities through a common program of material and political struggle.

b. Comrade Grau is also said to have compared the Union of Soviet Socialist Republics to Imperial Rome. If this was done to bring out the structural contrast between a modern alliance system and the ancient Imperial system, it can only be applauded. If the comparison was made to imply some similarity, Comrade Grau must be corrected.

c. All those who have protested about the speech are agreed that Comrade Grau made some justifiable points of criticism against the Rakosi clique. For instance, the failure to understand the criminal

nature of agriculture subversion during the spring
of last year. However, Grau is said to have linked
these failures to the presence of U.S.S.R. advisers
in Hungary. It is a detail, but it is said that Comrade Grau attributed poor news broadcasting in
the park as somehow the fault of U.S.S.R. communications advisers. This sort of petty, infantile
sniping is simply unworthy of a member of this
Party.

d. The most serious charge lodged against Comrade
Grau's speech concerns his concluding remarks.
He framed the relations between the U.S.S.R. and
Hungary in adversarial terms, and then implied
that the experience of civil counterrevolution
presented an opportunity for the Hungarian "side"
to win concessions from the U.S.S.R. "side."

After much discussion, the Ethnic Minorities Section
decided that the very possibility of making such charges
against Comrade Grau, whether or not they are true, im-
pairs his value to the Party. How is this possibility to be
explained?

We reject the idea that Comrade Grau is a secret spy,
like Laszlo Rajk. Comrade Grau served the socialist cause
well in 1919, throughout the 1930's, and in the war
against Fascism. No, we believe these lapses into religion
and signs of hostility against our friend and partner have
arisen simply because of Comrade Grau's advanced age.
We believe that the harm his presence now does the Party
should be stopped, and we believe the harm he does himself can be stopped if he is allowed to spend his twilight
years in a nursing home.

Some men, as they come to the end of their lives,

gather in the fruits of wisdom. They become ever more judicious. They are the sages and prophets celebrated in people's memories. Others are not so fortunate. The fear of death makes them falter. They are driven back into their childhood; they return to the magical, prescientific fantasies with which they were lulled as children. Does not the presence of Comrade Grau in churches, his reading of fairy tales, show his lapsing into this tragic condition of senility? Indeed, it is said that in his speech to Comrade Stos, he told an allegorical story about frogs. Justice to the Revolution demands that Comrade Grau no longer participate in the Party. Charity to this valiant, if now tired, fighter demands that we make his second childhood as comfortable as possible, in one of our nursing homes on the shores of Lake Balaton.

I responded to these charges in a memorandum filed with the Membership Committee of the Hungarian Communist Party:

Memorandum concerning membership in the Hungarian Communist Party, filed March 1, 1957, by Tibor Grau, Professor of Philosophy, University of Budapest

To the Membership Committee:

Gentlemen,
You have received a complaint from the Ethnic Minorities Section of the Party about my supposed behavior and statements during the recent counterrevolutionary incidents. I believe any fair-minded person will see in this complaint only a continuation of the tactics which prevailed during the time of the cult of personality. I am

accused of deviationism, in effect, when what I in fact advocate is a renewed revolutionary struggle. We all know how such charges were used by the Rakosi clique. However, I shall do these outmoded persons who accuse me an honor they withhold from me: I shall take their charges seriously.

Let me begin with the most inflammatory of their supposed complaints: they say I showed insufficient respect for the U.S.S.R. comrades and colleagues. But it is *I* who argued for continued cooperation with our comrades at a historical moment when many elements in the nation were calling for separation. It was *I* who exposed the myth of neutrality. It was *I* who called for an end to violence. It was *I* who denounced the American imperialists as illusory friends.

None of the members of the Ethnic Minorities Section was present at my speech. Unfortunately, I did not retain a copy of my remarks, and in any event, I spoke only from sketchy notes. So the proof I can offer you rests solely in the memory of my five listeners that day. I have spoken last week to our U.S.S.R. comrade and friend Stos, who confirms that these were the substantive points I made. While I have not been able, for various reasons, to speak to the other members at that meeting, I am sure they will concur with Comrade Stos, who, after all, represents the nation I am said to have aggrieved.

Specifically, I compared the U.S.S.R. to Imperial Rome only to show the white-and-black contrast between the two. I did speak of faulty communications equipment on the propaganda trucks, but gentlemen, if we do not criticize what exists, how can we make it better? I want those trucks to broadcast a clear message. Is this desire good grounds for my expulsion from the Hungarian Communist Party? People who cannot understand such an elemental point are clearly incapable of understanding my discussion of the dialectical processes of renewal, the context in which my remark about "sides," "satellites," and the like were made, all of which language I exposed. I do not require of the Ethnic Minorities Section that they be trained philosophers; I do require that people untrained in scientific ideological analysis not attempt to interpret through hearsay my statements shaped by a lifetime of hard study of Marxism-Leninism.

The depth of their misunderstanding is revealed in what they say they have heard about my allusion to frogs. This accusation echoes the incomprehension with which, nearly forty years ago, my edict about the conservation of folk tales was greeted during the revolutionary struggle of 1919. Now, as then, people do not appreciate the glory of our oral heritage, the tales and songs that constitute the culture of the people, a true culture unsullied by the self-doubts, the individualistic wallowing in so-called high art, of bourgeois decadence. The Ethnic Minorities ought to appreciate my love of the spontaneous outpourings of the people. But no, they accuse me, for my love of folk tales depicted by Grimm and others, as some sort of revolutionary lapse, whereas it is they who should be ashamed to be so unappreciative.

Consider the ideological situation of the frog in nature. A pure and unaggressive animal, who desires to live, to do no other animal harm. An animal without teeth. Is it any wonder that the frog is so celebrated in our folk tales by ordinary people? They, too, are pure and unaggressive. When I was Deputy Director of Cultural Propaganda in the old days, I sought to make Hungarians aware that folk tales about frogs were the way the oppressed attempted to think about a life-transcending oppression; these tales were a form of ideological construction of liberation before the advent of a scientific ideology of liberation could make the desires of the people realizable.

When I was a boy in Budapest, I would promenade in the Municipal Park at sunset, and hear welling up from the hollows the song of frogs. I have heard this song all my life, gentlemen. They accuse me of being old. I accept the charge. I am old. And the burden of being old is that you remember. I have seen over and over again our movement threatened by elements seeking personal gain. I can also remember a time when there was no hope, when men were starving in the park, men sleeping in trees. I have said so much about these particular animals, you see, because I do have these memories, and they mean so much to me I wish I could tell you, but the very length of time they have aged in my mind, so that their substance is faded while the sense of having them remains strong, means I couldn't tell you.

So then, this is my defense.

Two final points. It was said I saw a struggle between hooligans and police, yet did nothing to help. There was nothing I could do. It was said I have been seen in and near churches. Yes, I have been, because I want to be with people my own age. I am a materialist, you need have no worry on that score. But in times of trouble, people who have suffered through events draw close to each other. Unfortunately, most of the people my age grew up in an era in which the gods still appeared to men as a refuge, relieving the human race of the necessity to struggle for itself. You cannot blame these people for seeking the consolation of my comrades, those who can remember what I can because we were thrown into life at the same time. And you must take into account the fact that I never asked to be born.

In sum, I have been maligned by hearsay, misunderstood, and it is up to my accusers to defend themselves, to explain why they, so-called ethnic minorities, have no folk feeling, why they libel my acts of comradeship with my own peers as senility.

Such as I am, I remain to serve the Party until my dying day.

Memorandum No. 874, March 10, 1957
Membership Committee
Hungarian Communist Party

The membership committee is pleased to accede to the request of Comrade Tibor Grau to retire from active status in the Hungarian Communist Party. Comrade Grau has served the world Communist movement with distinction. He will be remembered as the Deputy Director of Cultural Propaganda in the Revolution of 1919, as a distinguished member of the Minsk Academy of Literature, as a valiant fighter against Fascism in the last war, and for more recent services. His writings have brought glory to himself and his cause throughout the world. When others doubted, he remained steadfast. Although born into the bourgeoisie, he from an early age acquired a radical consciousness of workers and their needs, he subordinated himself to these needs, and so was able to act forcefully on the stage of world history.

In token of all his services, we are pleased to grant him emeritus status at the University of Budapest. We wish him well in retirement. He will ever remain close to us in memory, a shining example of the new man our Revolution aims to produce.

My friend says to me these events illustrate the irony of history. The powerful always punish good men with lies. But here we come to the whole point of my story. My friend is wrong! I tried to help my countrymen; I spoke out. Yet, miraculously, I am still alive and well.